DATE DUE	DATE DUE	DATE DUE

1/98   c:/CIRC/DateDue.p65-p.14

WATER AND WATER USE TERMINOLOGY

*Observe at least once, in your short life span,
the fragile web of pristine values
intrinsic to a virgin lake or stream.*

*Should this experience be available
to posterity?*

WATER
AND
WATER USE
TERMINOLOGY

J. O. VEATCH
PROFESSOR EMERITUS
Soil Science Department
Michigan State University

C. R. HUMPHRYS
PROFESSOR
Department of Resource Development
Michigan State University

KAUKAUNA, WISCONSIN
THOMAS PRINTING & PUBLISHING CO., LTD.

PREFACE

With rapidly increasing population and technologic expansion in industry, there has come an increasing appreciation of the value of water. Because of the enormous present demand, and even greater prospective demand for water for industrial and municipal supplies for irrigation and recreation, water bodies, both natural and artificial, of all kinds have taken on tremendous social significance and money value, and their conservation has become a matter of great concern. With the increase in importance of water bodies, there comes a corresponding increase in need for basic knowledge and facts of all kinds about them. This compilation, called for convenience *Water and Water Use Terminology* has been made with the notion that it can be helpful in promoting a better understanding of water features especially those commonly known as lakes and ponds.

This publication is intended to be a kind of manual, a reference for the meaning of terms, for the use of those who are interested in, or concerned with the study of lakes as a natural resource. It is not restricted to Limnology, but is concerned with lakes, standing waters and related wetlands, in all aspects. It includes geologic, economic, geomorphologic, hydrologic, hydrographic, limnologic, ecologic and engineering terms; and some of a legal nature as well as terms pertaining to use, management and conservation, and in addition a large number of colloquial terms, localisms and rare or infrequent hydronyms.

The authors have been somewhat arbitrary and subjective in the matter of number and kinds of terms included in this work. The list of entries could be extended indefinitely if all related technical terms and all the known names of aquatic organisms and organic and inorganic compounds found in lakes, were included. Such an undertaking would require the collaboration of a large number of specialists, and even if accomplished would make the terminology so weighty and imbalanced as to defeat its primary purpose.

In the treatment of terms, the authors have, in most instances, attempted to be brief and concise, and have made free use of the device of cross reference and have used illustrations to further amplify and clarify meanings. A few terms and concepts which are believed to be new and original have been inserted.

J. O. VEATCH

C. R. HUMPHRYS

vii

FOREWORD

At the turn of the century, President Theodore Roosevelt with the able assistance of Gifford Pinchot, firmly established forest and mineral conservation in the philosophy and economy of our country. Rapid utilization, misuse and waste set the stage for wholesale dedication of remaining public domain lands as National forests, parks and mineral reserves. Under federal jurisdiction the people would be insured of continuing protection and management programs for these resources.

In 1934 the ominous "dust cloud" from the Great Plains provided Hugh Hammond Bennett a spectacular vehicle upon which to carry the nation into the era of soil conservation. In this instance, ownership of the resource was not transferred to the federal government. Technical expertise and subsidies were provided as incentives to those who needed assistance.

Both of these conservation ideologies were conceived on a bed of waste, ignorance and flagrant misuse and born in an atmosphere of violent economic and political change. Both were heralded into existence by evangelists of conservation — Gifford Pinchot and Hugh Hammond Bennett were both idealists with pronounced ability to mold opinion. Public opinion was caught in a thunderous backwash of moral and ethical guilt and swept out to sea to start anew, with conservation programs that are now considered epoch landmarks in the history of the world.

More lately, our nation is experiencing a virtual "flood" of conservation problems — this time, the waste and misuse concerns water. Few people in the United States can escape the knowledge of its presence. Rachel Carson has set a spark to our national conscience. *Silent Spring* may well have been the prelude to still another new and dramatic era of resource management. Rachel has passed on, but new leaders will arise to guide thought and action towards an eventual solution of our imposing water resource problems.

The nebulous fabric of our existing conservation philosophy is again taking the form of a uniform representative of a moral, legal and ethical crusade to correct old and painful wrongs.

The new and very ugly threat to water resources does not vitally concern us only with scarcity, surplus or erosion, but with the oppressive debasement and defilement resulting from the greatly increased magnitude of sewage disposal and toxic effluents of all kinds. Damage to *water quality* involves direct economic costs for treatment that are tangible and may be appropriately surveyed, analysed and interpreted into monetary costs and taxes. These things we know and understand, however the unknown and misunderstood damage to the aesthetic qualities of water must be at least uncovered for public scrutiny and appraisal before control is possible. *Knowledge must proceed public action.*

This book brings together many of the words, terms and expressions of the various arts and sciences which contribute to the knowledge of water resources. In our language, each art and science has its own peculiar or specific interpretation of water. The derivation and use of each specific term has also frequently changed from the time of its original conception.

Eventually, a new and more precise language of water will emerge, but its origin and geneology will reflect our past efforts in the definition of physical water character along with the hope of preserving the intangible characteristics of water which are easily dismissed or forgotten in our busy, modern, hard and practical world.

C. R. Humphrys

TOPICS COVERED

BACTERIOLOGY	Aesthetics
	Aging of Lakes
BOTANY	Aquatic Plants
	Artificial Lakes
CARTOGRAPHY	Deed Restrictions
ECOLOGY	Drainage
	Islands
ECONOMICS	Lake Access
	Lake Classification
ENGINEERING	Lake Development
GEOGRAPHY	Lake Improvements
	Lake Management
GEOLOGY	Lake Problems
	Lake Use
GEOMORPHOLOGY	Lakeshore Classification
	Platting
HYDROGRAPHY	Pollution
HYDROLOGY	Public Health
	Real Estate Development
LACOLOGY	Recreation
	Reservoirs
LAW	Soils
	Surface Water
LIMNOLOGY	Water Management Structures
PEDOLOGY	Water Quality
	Water Rights
SURVEYING	Zoning

NEW WORDS

Neologisms

Neologisms are newly coined words, phrases or expressions. The interests, competition and conflicts involved with water resources have created a definite need for new words that are descriptive of present day knowledge. Final acceptance and continued use of these new words is always problematical, however they do have an intrinsic value as a means of introducing new ideas and philosophy that would otherwise not be included in a text of this nature.

NEW WORDS

aquamarsh
canalized subdivision
cryolimnon
eoshoreline
extralegal access
extralegal riparian
fission lakes
fusion lakes
Lacology
limited access (lake)
litigious littoral
lot-water ratio (of a lake)
man-property value ratio (lake)
necfluve (lake)
neoshoreline
nova lakes
over-developed lake
paludolac
paradox lakes
phantom drain
purgatorial reliction (inland lakes)
quondam island (in lake basin)
quondam outlets
smirchment, lake
spate ponds
suffosion lakes
telmaro
train of lakes
vicinage (lake)

WATER
AND
WATER USE
TERMINOLOGY

abandoned boats

Abandoned boats become an aggravating problem when boating safety and the aesthetics of the lake are involved. Strictly enforced registration regulations and legal authority to remove abandoned boats, at the expense of the owner, will alleviate this problem.

abandonment of a dam

In a legal sense, abandonment is most precisely described as transfer of all rights, title and interest in a dam to the current property owner.

Abandonment may also involve the slow but resolute erosion of rights to a dam by non-use, physical destruction, lack of maintenance or intent of same. In this latter instance the final determination of legal abandonment can only be decided by the court holding jurisdiction.

abioseston

Nonliving components of the seston.

See: *seston*

abyssal depth (lakes)

In a limnological sense, that depth at which the water remains uniform in temperature, or is "stagnant".

access (to a lake)
> See: *easement access*
> *funnel access*
> *lake access*
> *public access*

accretion
A term denoting the process by which *alluvion* is made. However, the two words, *accretion* and *alluvion*, are often used synonymously.
> See: *alluvion*
> *reliction*

acidity (lake water)
Ordinarily expressed as a pH below 7.

acre foot (of water)
An area of one acre covered to a depth of one foot. One acre foot of stored water in a reservoir, lake, or pond will give a flow of 20 miner's inches (one-half cubic foot per second) of water for 24 hours. One acre foot is 43,560 cubic feet or 325,851 gallons.

Aerbacter aerogenes
These bacteria are common in soil and decaying matter. Lakewater collected near the shore will usually show a positive coliform test and should not be used for drinking purposes.
> See: *coliform bacteria*

aesthetics (lake)
Aesthetics are given consideration in the complete evaluation of lakes as a natural resource. The overall scenic attraction of the lake setting; natural beauty of shores and

waters, or any unusual natural phenomena; the appeal of its wildlife and aquatic plants; desirable natural landscape for homesites on the shores are some of the matters considered under this heading.

Photo – Michigan Department of Conservation

Natural beauty of shore and water.

aestival ponds

Those existing only in summer.

affluent (of a lake)

A tributary or feeder stream. Streams receiving the run-off from the watershed and flowing into the lake are its *affluents;* analogous to the affluent of a river. The analogy can be very close where a lake has large inflowing and outflowing streams and is located in a valley or elongated basin. In usage, the term may have the same meaning as *influent;* although where the reference is to a single inflowing stream, the word *influent* appears to be the preferred one.

      See: *influent*
           inlet

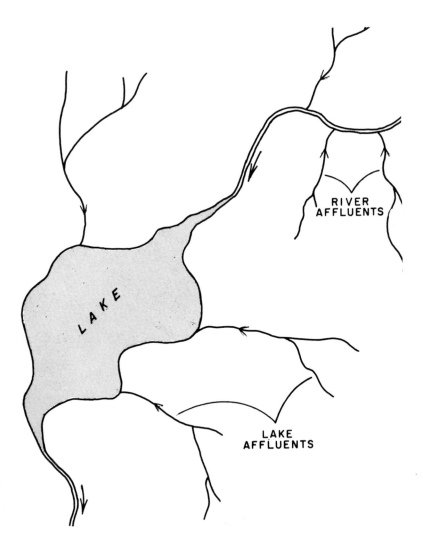

afterbay

A tail race; the term is also sometimes applied to a pond or reservoir.

aging, of a lake

A condition which affects the life span. Enrichment of the waters, prolific growth of aquatic vegetation, and filling accelerate *aging* and shorten the life of the lake.

agua

This Spanish word for water is occasionally used in Southwestern U. S. in names of bodies of water such as lakes and lagoons, as well as springs.

Algae

A term for an assemblage of non-vascular plants consisting of a great number of genera and species both microscopic and large in size; in large part aquatic and growing in both sea water and fresh water. In ponds and lakes the "pond scums", "blooms" and Chara or *stonewort*, are classified as Algae. Algae are commonly placed in phyla which have a characteristic pigment color: blue green; green; yellow green; brown; and red.

Algae carry on photosynthesis which differentiates them from *fungi*.

See: *Chara*
water bloom

Prolific growth of algae on Shagawa Lake, Ely, Minnesota.

algae wash

Shoreline drift composed mainly of filamentous algae. The plants are carried to the shore by wind and wave action and stranded at or near the limit of wave advance. The drift often accumulates in considerable quantity and can become highly obnoxious on beaches.

algicide

Any substance which kills algae. Algae can become highly obnoxious in lakes, and therefore control measures are sought. Chemicals containing copper, such as copper sulphate, are commonly employed for the control of algae "blooms".

alkali lakes

Those containing water with very high concentrations of alkalies. The "alkali" may be sodium carbonate or sodium sulphate and potassium carbonate but includes other alkaline compounds as well. Restricted to arid and semi-arid regions.

See: *potash lakes*
soda lakes

alkalinity (lake waters)

Ordinarily expressed as a pH above 7. Most lake water in the alkaline class has a range from pH 7.6 to 9.

Alkalinity may be expressed as the amounts of carbonates, bicarbonates and hydroxides present in the water. Alkalinity is expressed in parts per million, under the names of dyes, used as indicators in the tests, as methyl orange (M. O. A.), methyl purple (M. P. A.) and phenolphthalein.

allochthonous detritus

Particulate matter originating outside, and carried into the lake.

alluvial dam lakes

Numerous basins which are the sites of both existing and extinct lakes in the arid regions of western U. S. were formed by alluvial dams, especially by the coalescence of fans composed of detritus carried down by streams from opposite sides of valleys. In glaciated regions dams were formed in valleys by glacio-fluvial deposition during the Pleistocene; and barriers of various kinds, which impound water, have been created in river flood plains by alluvial deposition.

See: *fluviatile lakes*
levee lakes

alluvion (lake)

In its legal meaning, alluvion is an accretion to land, made gradually, composed of detritus deposited by streams or of deposits accumulated by the action of waves and currents.

On lakes, accretions are made: by alluvial deposition on the advancing front of a delta; by filling of shoreline lake bottom by erosion detritus carried in by affluents, gullies and superficial surface run-off or rainwash; by shifting dune sand; and by waste disposal such as tailings from mine operations. Also natural accretions may be made to islands, bars and beaches of lakes. The deposits are realities, but whether or not, in specific instances, they constitute legal alluvion which involves land ownership is, ultimately, a matter for court decisions.

See: *reliction*

alluvium (lake)

The sediments, or detrital matter, carried by inflowing streams and deposited on lake bottoms.

alpine lakes

Lakes in any high mountain region, associated with snow, ice and a cold climate.

amenities (of a lake)

Those features or aspects which produce a pleasurable effect, have a sentimental value or contribute to comfort.

amphibian cottage

A cottage constructed partially on the land and partially on piling in the water of a lakeshore. This unique structure features a car port on the land side and a boat well on the lake side, all under the same roof.

anchor ice

Ice which extends down to and is attached, or frozen, to the lake bottom. Also called bottom ice; depth ice; ground ice.

anchorage and storage

With the great increase in boating and water sports of all kinds, more and more submerged lands are being dedicated to the storage of water sports equipment. Frequently the shoreline is modified by dredging and weed removal to accomodate the various structures used with boating. On some lakes a high percentage of the shoreline has been pre-empted for wharfage thereby excluding some other uses of shallow water.

Some craft, such as sailboats, require considerable area for safe anchorage. This use may become great enough to reduce the total usable area of a lake. Inadequate parking space for automobiles has been cited as a limiting factor in the use of public beaches; inadequate anchorage space may also be a limiting factor in the use of the lake surface.

antagonism, pollution

Antagonism is the opposite of *synergism.* Two toxicants reacting may have a lesser adverse total effect than the sum of the two toxicants acting separately.

See: *synergism, pollution*

aphotic zone

See: *euphotic zone*

aphytal

The plantless zone of a lake bottom; the profundal.

appropriation doctrine

Under the doctrine of prior appropriation water is subject to appropriation for beneficial use. The person first granted appropriation has exclusive prior rights, and each succeeding appropriation has prior rights over the following one. Basic principles of this doctrine are recognized in most of the Western States.

Aqua

This word may be used as the generic in a place name for a body of water such as a lake or reservoir. Instances of such use, however, are infrequent.

aquamarsh

A water body in which the original open water is nearly or completely obscured by emergent, and floating aquatic vegetation. A stage in the evolution between open water and land marsh.

See: *paludolac*

Transition between open water and marsh.

aquaponics

The culture of plants in water areas (which includes lakes) in contrast to cultivation of plants on land, or geoponics.

aquasol

A water soil. Water is the medium in which the plants grow.

See: *Hydrosol*

aquatic plants (lake)

The aquatic plants of lakes and other kinds of standing water bodies are those whose seeds germinate in the water or in the lake bottom soil; those that grow in water and are commonly grouped as floating, submerged and emergent. The aquatics are *Hydrophytes;* this latter category also includes plants which tolerate wet conditions, grow in a saturated soil but are not restricted to water covered sites. Some plants growing in lakes are *hydrophytic,* but not strictly aquatic.

aquiculture

The production of plants and animals under management in bodies of water. Aquiculture is broader in meaning than *hydroponics* inasmuch as it may include the production of crops from natural water bodies such as lakes. Examples of aquicultural products are: fish, rice and cranberries.

area (of a lake)

The space occupied by the water surface.

The area of a lake, generally, is something that cannot be determined with great exactitude; often the figure given is an arbitrary one, and figures from different sources often show considerable disagreement. This comes about, because some error is inherent in any of the procedures devised for determining area; because measurements may be made from hydrographic maps which differ in accuracy and detail, and in time at which the map was made. This latter becomes important where lakes fluctuate greatly in levels. Some differences may arise also where different mathematical procedures are followed in making the measurements. Also, often arbitrary decisions must be made as to location of shoreline, the inclusion or exclusion of islands, and boundaries between a lake and a connecting water, all of which consequently affect the computed area. The area of some lakes in the arid parts of U. S. may vary greatly year to year, or even often month to month; and under some circumstances in humid regions, water in lime sink lakes may disappear completely and reappear at some later time. Area is usually expressed in square miles and acres; or where the metric system is used in square kilometers and square meters.

See: *size*

arm (of a lake)
A long and relatively narrow body of water extending inland from the main body. Usually the term *arm* is applied to a reach of water, greater in length and narrower than one called a *bay*, but often on maps no clear distinction exists between *arm* and *bay* nor between *arm* and *lobe*.

articulation (of a lake)
The ratio of area of inlets and bays to the total area of the lake.

artificial (lakes, ponds)

Basins purposely excavated by man and filled with water by catchment from run-off, by pumping or by diversion of natural water bodies. Definitely artificial are those ponds constructed for farm use, for receiving factory wastes, sewage, etc. However, there are degrees of artificiality. Bodies of water impounded by dams across rivers are artificial only to a degree as are lakes whose basins have been altered by dredging or filling or whose levels have been raised or lowered respectively by dams across outlets or by dredging outlets. A gravel pit or stone quarry is patently an artificial basin, but its filling with water, after abandonment, may be a natural process. Ponds occupying mine cave-in pits can hardly be accepted as natural geomorphological features, neither are they intentionally constructed and filled with water by man. Wherever man has made use of the water or occupied the adjacent land, he has modified natural lakes to some degree, and to that degree made them artificial. The number of *wilderness* lakes is fast diminishing and the number of artificial lakes rapidly increasing.

artificial beach

A bathing beach created by removing peat or muck and subsequent filling with sand or fine gravel. Sand may also be spread over a clay shore to create a more desirable beach. Occasionally sand is placed on a polyethelene (plastic) blanket which has been spread over soft bottom, but this kind of beach is not considered permanent.

Groins are frequently constructed on the Great Lakes shoreline to trap shore drift thereby creating a desirable beach.

Association (lake)

A voluntary union of riparians whose purpose is management or development, or use or conservation of riparian lands and lake surface. Their union may vary from a gentlemen's agreement or may be in the form of a profit or non-profit corporation. In some instances the prospective buyer must become a member of the lake association as a condition to the purchase of frontage; continuous membership in the association becomes part of the purchase contract.

atoll moor

A term which has been applied to a peat bog which entirely surrounds a *lake* in the form of a ring, and is in turn surrounded by a "ditch" or ring of open water around the original shoreline of the lake. The term "sphagnum atoll" has also been applied to some bogs. (References to these features and citations of literature were made by C. A. Davis, Peat, *Geological Survey*, Michigan, Annual Report, 1906, pages 128 and 154).

See: *moat lake*

aufwuchs

Aufwuchs includes all those organisms that are attached to a submerged substrate but do not penetrate into its surface. This term is broader and more inclusive than *periphyton;* aufwuchs includes crustaceans, insects and other forms.

autochthonous detritus

Particulate matter originating in the lake.

avigational trespass

Persons using a float plane to gain access to a private

lake without permission, trespass first on the air or aviga-
tional rights of the lake owners, then by landing on the
surface of the lake, they commit simple trespass.

avja-gyttja
Lake bottom deposit composed largely of remains of
algae.
See: *gyttja*

avulsion, lakeshore
Marked changes in the shore of a lake, extensive removal and redeposition of soil, are sometimes produced
by wave erosion during a severe storm. These changes
affect riparian property and legal questions arise about
changes in property lines and ownership of transported
and redeposited material.

back lots (of a lake)

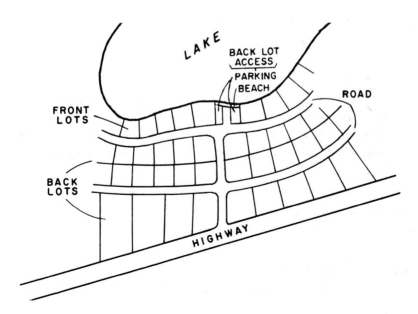

Platted lots lying back of the frontage lands of a lake and therefore having no direct water access to the lake. The owners of these lots may, however, enjoy access to the lake via exclusive or semi-exclusive access or by virtue of a community beach dedicated to their joint use and enjoyment.

See: *lake subdivision*

backland (lake)

See: *beach profile* for illustration
environment for illustration

In a geomorphic sense the lake recession lowland (usually swamp or marsh) that lies back of the present shoreline, or between it and the old shoreline, or *eoshore*. Backland is also applied to the bordering land area back of the water frontage for an indeterminate distance.

See: *eoshore*

backrush

Same as *backwash*.
See: *backwash*

backshore

See: *beach profile* for illustration

That portion of the beach lying inshore from the beach crest. It is usually flatter than the foreshore and is often divided by low scarps formed by cutting during severe storms. The backshore is also often a berm.

See: *beach*

backwash

The flow of water down the foreshore following the uprush of a wave.

See: *swash*
wake

backwater

The upstream effect, for a distance back of a dam, which appears as an increase in depth and expansion in the width of the stream and a slackening in the current. Also the stagnant water which has backed up in side channels and in the depressions of a flood plain as a result of river floods. *Backwater* is used as the equivalent of other terms such as *reservoir, lake, pond, basin or flow-age* and may appear in the geographic name of an impoundment.

bacteria, lake

Bacteria are present in practically all natural lakes and ponds. They are found in association with lake bottom muds and the digestive tracts of animals.

Where man is a factor in the environment, pathogenic bacteria can occur, especially where sewage and sewage effluent is present.

See: *Aerobacter aerogenes*
coliform bacteria
Escherichia coli
most probable number of coliform bacteria
pathogenic bacteria

bait dealer

One who sells live bait to fisherman.

banco

An ox-bow lake. (local in Texas)

bank

Pertaining to a lake, the sharply rising ground, or abrupt slope, usually wave-cut and presenting a nearly vertical front, bordering the shore or water line. In usage not precisely limited to a minimum or maximum height; and not consistently distinguished from *cliff* and *bluff*; usually applied to clay and sand and only rarely to bedrock. *Bank* also appears in literature as a term for a shoal bottom of a lake, but this usage is not common. Also, the scarp, or drop-off, of a subaqueous terrace or littoral shelf of a lake may be called a *bank* in hydrographic descriptions. In some places along the Atlantic Coast the long narrow island of sand which forms a barrier between the inland lagoon, or sound, and the sea is called a *bank*.

bank rights
See: *riparian rights*

bar (lake)
An embankment of sand, gravel, or other detritus carried by shore currents and deposited in the form of spits

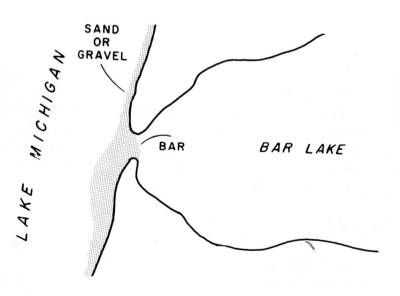

connecting two headlands, or across shore indentations or embayments. Bars may be submerged, or may be built above water.

The ends of a bar need not be attached to the land. In this respect a *bar* may differ from a *spit*.

See: *spit*

bar lake

A popular name for a lake which has a sand bar across its outlet. The bar is not necessarily a cause, by impoundment, for the lake; it may have been deposited after the formation of the lake. A number of bar lakes, of the drowned valley type, occur along the east coast of Lake Michigan.

barren shoal

Shallow lake bottom which is nearly devoid of aquatic plant growth.

barrier lake

See: *lagoon*

Basin (impoundment)

Basin is used in several locations in Michigan as a generic, a part of a place name, for an area of water back of a dam. Here the word is used interchangeably with *reservoir, pond, lake,* and *flowage*. In a few places, the impoundment is called a *Storage Basin*.

basin (lake)

The submerged part of a bowl, trough or any other form of depression which holds the water of a lake. The rim of the basin is the high water mark or shoreline which marks the highest stage of water. The topography of a

Diagrammatic Lake Basin Profile

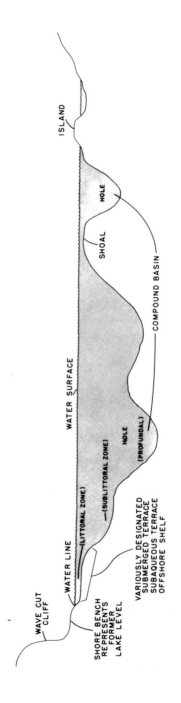

lake basin may be retained pretty much in its original form, or the basin may undergo considerable modification chiefly by filling often to the point of extinction of the water surface. Basins are recognized for extinct as well as living lakes, and their boundaries can be established by locating the old shorelines on the basis of any remaining evidence.

See: *hydrographic basin* (lake)

basin seal

Evidence exists that clay lining the bottoms and sides of lake basins in bed rock; and that colloids filling the interstices in sandy deposits (such as the outwash plains of Michigan) in which lake basins occur may form *seals* which prevent outseepage. Colloidal organic deposits may also act as a seal to prevent or lessen seepage.

Lacustrine deposits removed during a low level stage. The water level in the trench is 18 inches lower than the lake surface, illustrating the sealing effect of colloidal organic material.

bathing raft
> See: *diving raft*

bathymetric map
> Relating to depth measurements; a contour map of the submerged part of a lake basin.

bay (of inland lakes)
> A recess in the shoreline. Bay is not restricted to a single form or shape: a bay may be a lobe of water extending fairly deeply inland and enclosed by headlands; or the term may be applied to a bight or what is merely a shallow curve or arc in the shore between heads, as well as to narrow arms and inlets. In usage the term is not consistently distinguished from and is often used interchangeably with *cove, lobe, bight, arm, estuary,* and *bayou.*

bay head
> That portion of a bay which lies farthest inland from the main water body.

bay headland beach
> One formed at the end of a bay headland.

bay mouth
> That portion of the bay which is in contact with the main water body and serves as a connection with it. The entrance to a bay.

bayhead beach
> A beach formed at the head of a bay.
> See: *pocket beach*

baymouth bar

A bar across the mouth or entrance of a bay; one connecting the ends, or heads of the promontories, forming the enclosing sides of the bay.

bayou

A term variously applied to water features in the nature of bays, inlets, backwater, river channel sloughs, oxbow lakes, channels in coastal marshes and sluggish creeks. The geographic range of usage is generally considered to be restricted to Louisiana and other Gulf states, but bayou as a name for some of the water features mentioned is recognized northward also and appears on maps and as an element in place names in several localities in Michigan and other states.

bays (ponds)

Small and fairly large shallow closed basins, generally containing tree and shrub vegetation, but also in part open water, are a widely distributed feature of the flat upland of the lower part of the Atlantic Coastal Plain of Southeastern U. S., especially in the Carolinas, Georgia, and Florida. These are known generally by the localism "bay" but in some instances of usage *pocoson* is applied to the same kind of wetland feature. Probably most of the depressions are consequent, that is they are inherited from the land surface recently emerged from the sea, but some may be solution depressions. Also for those in the Carolinas a theory has been advanced that the depressions are craters made by meteoric shower impacts.

In southern Georgia and Florida the term "bay" is also applied locally to arms of swamps which extend as baylike indentations into the upland; and to the swampy "heads" of drainage ways.

beach

See: *beach profile* for illustration

The width of the shore zone lapped by waves. Technically this zone is composed of the *foreshore* and the *backshore*. Collateral terms are: *backshore, backwash, beach crest, spit, cusps, beach ridge, beach scarp, berm, nip, swash marks, beach, foreshore, plunge point, uprush, swash, wet beach, dry beach, storm beach, raised beach.* See these terms under their respective entries.

The beaches of inland lakes compared with those of oceans and the Great Lakes are weakly developed, and some kinds of inland lakes may have no beaches at all.

Beaches are commonly thought of as being composed of sand, but technically beaches are not limited to sands in texture; nor are they restricted in composition to any particular kind of rock mineral or other material.

beach crest

A ridge or berm that marks the landward limit of normal wave activity. A beach crest may be a temporary feature.

beach erosion

Gradual or catastrophic removal and destruction of beaches, especially sand beaches, by the erosive action of littoral currents or by the action of waves, ice shove and wind.

beach front

Land consisting of beach or that bordering a beach.

beach pool

(1) Any small incidental body of water back of the shoreline of a beach; (2) a lagoon back of a beach ridge.

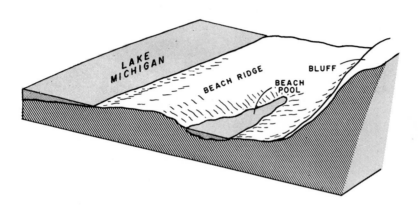

beach profile

A beach profile is a cross section of the dry beach and near offshore along a line perpendicular to the shoreline.

Diagram of Beach Profile

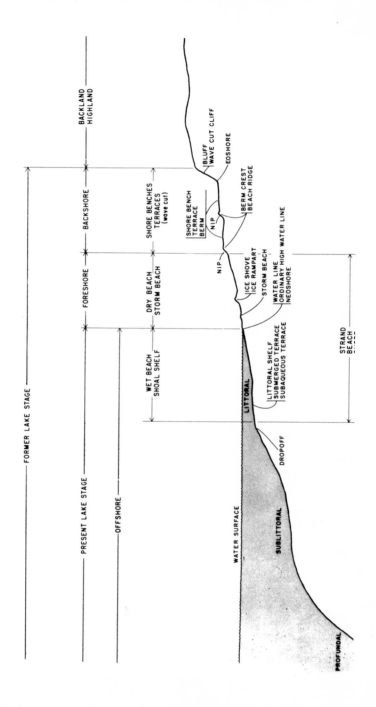

beach ridges

See: *beach profile* for illustration

Low roughly parallel ridges of sand, two or more are a fairly common feature of the shoreland of lakes, especially the Great Lakes in Michigan. The ridges may be closely spaced and separated by narrow trough-like depressions, or by wider flats which are generally wet. These depressional shoreline features have not been given an appropriate name.

Beach ridge in foreground, in process of formation; older ridge in background, and intervening swale.

They have been called *swales, slashes* and *furrows* but none of these are particularly apt or fitting inasmuch as they also have been applied to other kinds of minor natural features, and *slash* and *furrow* have various other meanings not related to natural land forms.

beach scarp
> The near vertical face of a beach ridge.

beachline
> The word does not connote a line, but rather the *strand,* or *beach,* itself, which is a narrow belt appearing as a line especially when depicted on a map.
>
> Sometimes a distinction between *strand* and *beach* is observed, but most often the two are used interchangeably and also often no sharp distinction is observed between these two terms and *shoreline.*

beaver meadow
> See: *beaver ponds*

beaver ponds
> Ponds, or lakes, and floodings formed back of dams built by the American beaver, *Castor canadensis.* These features were numerous throughout northern states at the time of early settlement. The dams were usually built

Photo – U. S. Forest Service

A beaver dam and pond.

across a stream and a number at intervals often resulted in a chain of ponds and marshes. Where the dams were abandoned, the floodings changed into sedge and grass marshes, known as *beaver meadows*.

The beaver also built dams on pre-existing lakes and ponds, often raising their levels, but such water bodies are not properly *beaver ponds*, inasmuch as they are not entirely a consequence of the dam.

bed (lake)

Lake *bed* and lake *bottom*, generally are used interchangeably and refer to the submerged land surface of a lake basin. In some instances of usage "bed" is more specific in that it refers to the sedimentary deposits; also the land surface marking the site of a former lake is more likely to be called "lake bed".

>   See: *bottom*
>   *floor*

beneficial use

A term used especially in court decisions pertaining to the rights of riparians, and others, to use the waters of streams and lakes. A *beneficial use* has commonly been declared to be one that results in a material benefit, such as the use of water for the production of agricultural crops, or one that is profitable in a pecuniary sense. The trend in recent years is in favor of declaring recreational use of water to be a primary beneficial use.

>   See: *reasonable use*

benefits

The cost of improvement of lakes by dredging, diversion of water, building of dams, etc. may be assessed against individual parcels of land bordering the lake according to *benefits*. The *benefits* are the estimated advantages gained both of a tangible and intangible nature.

benthic zones

The bottom zones of a lake - *littoral, sublittoral,* and *profundal.*

benthos

A limnological term for the whole group of bottom dwelling organisms of a lake.

berm

See: *beach profile* for illustration

A low relatively flat bench lying between the high water mark on a shore and the cliff or scarp of bordering shore highland. Berms are a recognized feature of seashores and are recognized on the shores of the Great Lakes, but are not present, or if so are weakly developed, on the inland lakes.

bight

A broad, gradual bend or curve in a shoreline; a broad open bay; but contrarywise the word may also mean a segment of a bay or a narrow recess in a shoreline. The term is more commonly applied to shores of seacoasts, but does appear rarely in the description of inland waters.

bioassay

A test for water, suspected of being polluted, namely its effect on living organisms under standardized conditions.

biochemical oxygen demand

The amount of dissolved oxygen in parts per million, required by organisms and for the aerobic biochemical decomposition of organic matter present in water. This determination may be made by any of several acceptable laboratory techniques. A test for biochemical oxygen demand is standard procedure for public health, pollution control and conservation agencies.

Sewage treatment plant effluents are commonly tested for biochemical oxygen demand; industrial effluents are also tested by pollution control agencies in order to establish required levels of treatment.

biomass

See: *standing crop*

biscuit marl

See: *marl biscuit*

bitter lakes

Those containing large amounts of sulphates such as magnesium sulphate in their waters. In usage, restricted to the arid regions in the United States.

black sands

Concentrations of black minerals, such as magnetite (Fe_3O_4), in layers in the littoral deposits of lakes, are not uncommon where such minerals are abundant in the detritus. Presumably the concentration took place because the black minerals were sorted, due to their higher specific gravity, as the sands were agitated by wave action.

blanket moss

A demotic for a formation of filamentous algae. In very fertile ponds, or lakes, and in sheltered areas near shore, filamentous green algae sometimes attain an excessively prolific growth and appear in the form of dense mats or "blankets".

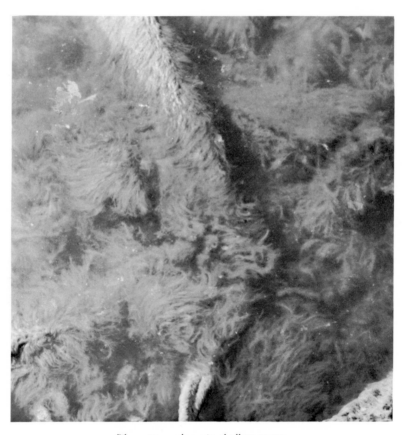

Filamentous algae in shallow water.

blast holes

A new blasting technique, utilizing nitrate fertilizer soaked in fuel oil and triggered by dynamite, makes the creation of small shallow pools (15 to 30 feet in diameter) in marsh and swampland economical and easy. These

Photo — Michigan Department of Conservation

Blast holes in a marsh with connecting level ditches.

pools provide open water habitat for ducks, geese and furbearers thereby increasing the biotic potential of these wetlands.

blight (lake frontage)
See: *lake frontage blight*

blind islands
A popular name for patches of marl, or organic deposits, with only a very shallow covering of water.
See: *sunken islands*

blind lake
A colloquialism for a lake that has neither an inflowing stream nor an outlet.

bloodworms
The larvae of midges; cylindrical in form, segmented up to 25mm in length. Some are blood red in color. Common in rich lakes. An important food for fishes.
See: *midges*

bloom (lake)
See: *water bloom*

blowout pond
A temporary shallow pool or pond that occupies a basin originally created by wind erosion. Ground water and surface runoff provide a source of water.
See: *deflation lakes*

A blowout pond on dune near Silver Lake, Michigan.

bluestone
A common name for the chemical, copper sulphate, used to control the growth of algae in farm ponds and lakes. Also called blue vitriol.

bluff (lake)
See: *beach profile* for illustration

The steep slopes, generally wave cut and nearly vertical and bare, rising from the shoreline of lakes, are called *cliffs, bluffs,* and *banks,* in usage, regardless of height and geologic composition. In technical descriptions *cliff* appears to be the preferred term. However, no consistent differences in meanings are recognized and the three are often used interchangeably.

See: *bank*

cliff (lakeshore)

boat basin

A protected anchorage for small water craft with facilities for launching and loading. The basin may be excavated from shoreland or created by a *breakwater*.

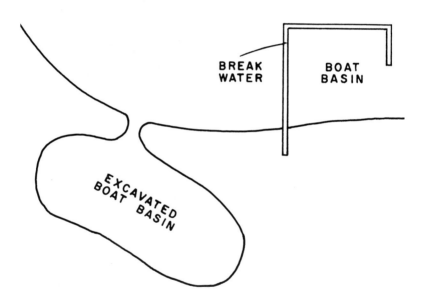

boat ditch

A narrow shallow canal cut through marsh or lake border lowland to provide isolated riparians with access to a lake. Sometimes the boat ditches appear to provide extralegal riparian rights to owners of inland tracts of land.

See: *extralegal riparian rights*

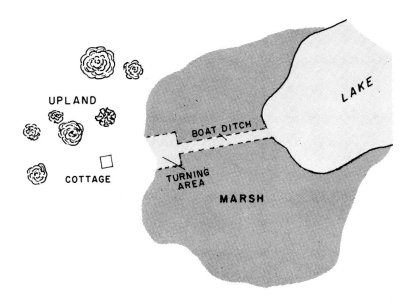

boat livery
A place on a lake shore, usually a dock, or a boat house, where boats are available to the public for hire.

boat ramp
A location on the shore of a lake where the slope is gentle enough to permit the use of cars and trailers for boat launching and loading. Trafficability may be improved by the installation of surfacing materials; sand, gravel, metal matting, macadam or concrete. Grading is frequently required to construct a safe slope.

The dramatic increase in small boat use combined with improved boat trailer development has required the construction of elaborate boat ramps at public lake access points.

See: *launching area*

boat slide

A localism in Northern Michigan for unimproved boat access to lakes with high banks.

boat slip

A narrow inland extension of the lake surface made by dredging to provide berthing facilities for small water craft. In connection with inland lakes the meaning, a space between two piers, is rarely recognized.

boat underpass

Roads passing over waterways between lakes may have special culverts installed to provide for the passage of small boats. The cross section of the boat underpass

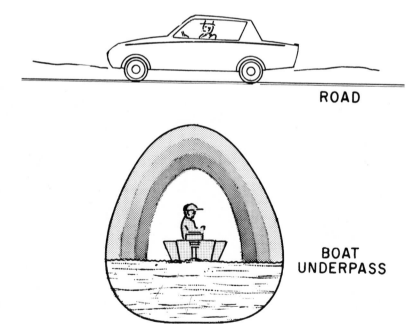

ROAD

BOAT
UNDERPASS

may be oval or angular but its basic design provides adequate width at the water level for the passage of a boat and height for head room.

boat well

An individual space along a boat dock or in a boat basin where a boat is tied. A *boat well* sometimes has decking on both sides for easy access.

boathouse

A structure built on the shoreline of a lake for the storage of boats. The structure may be built over water on piling or on a floating base, or on land and provided

Boathouse with living quarters on second floor.

with a ramp and a dry floor. Boat houses are sometimes commodious and elaborate, providing space for storage of recreational accessories, and some have second stories and sundecks.

B.O.D.
Abbreviation for biochemical oxygen demand.
See: *biochemical oxygen demand*

bog
The word *bog* in its wide sense refers to any wetland feature or body of land, characterized by a spongy, miry surface. The word is often used loosely, and often interchangeably with *marsh, swamp, muskeg,* moor and other wetland terms. Without a reference to a geographic or physiographic location, or some attributive indicating the kind of feature, the word has no precise connotation.

In the glaciated region of northern United States, and especially in the Lake States, the bogs are commonly peat bogs, and most frequently occur in basins; representing the sites of former lakes, or occur as formations partly or completely surrounding existing lakes. Bogs are further differentiated according to the characteristic surface vegetation such as sphagnum moss, leather leaf, and the conifers black spruce, tamarack and white cedar. However, where in the ecologic succession the tree vegetation becomes dominant the term *swamp* often replaces "bog" in usage. Likewise *marsh* may replace *bog* for very large treeless wetland areas characterized by grasses and sedges.

The term *quaking bog* is commonly applied to sedge-grass mats on the margins of lakes, and other semi-floating types of peat in lake basins.
See: *marsh*
swamp

bog lake

A lake or small open body of water surrounded completely or nearly so by a bog formation — characteristic vegetation, leatherleaf, sphagnum moss, black spruce, etc., growing either on a firm deposit or a semi-floating mat of acid peat. In some potholes, or kettles, the open water may be a narrow zone, or moat, bordering the periphery or shore; other transitional conditions between shallow

A bog lake in Northern Michigan.

water and complete filling, but with subsurface water at shallow depths, exist which may be arbitrarily designated as either *bog lake* or *bog*. In Michigan, *bog lake* and *muskeg lake* have the same meaning.

Some common characteristics of bog lakes are: acidity or pH below 7; soft water; dark colored water; soft, "mud" or peaty, bottoms; false bottoms and soft shores.

bog walkway

A permanent or temporary structure laid on floating bog or soft shore to provide access to the open water of a lake.

boiling spring

See: *spring lake*

bold

A high cliff, cape, head or promontory rising from the water. More often applied to bold features on sea coasts, but not inappropriate for lakes.

boom

A floating structure of logs, used to protect a dam or other structure built in the water, from wave action or from damage by floating debris.

booming logs for pulp

Logs for pulp are still transported to mills by towing booms with a tug through lakes and inland waterways. A boom chain or cable is equipped with floats and passed around a boom of floating pulp logs. A tug then tows the boom to the mill.

borax, lacustrine

Borax ($Na_2B_4O_7$) occurs dissolved in some lake waters in arid regions, notably in the brines of Searles and Owens Lakes in California.

borrow pit ponds

Artificial ponds which fill excavations made in obtaining sand, gravel or other material usually for subgrades and fills in highway construction. Such ponds are common along new highways and may remain either temporary or as permanent features. Some borrow pits have been modified for intensive recreational use and have been formally named as lakes.

bottom (lake)

Bottom is the land, or ground, lying beneath the water. In usage of the term *lake bottom,* the reference may be merely to the surface of the submerged land, its horizontality, inclination, or relief; or secondly the reference may be to the composition and physical nature of the sedimentary deposition in the lake, or to that of the formation composing the sides and floor of the basin.

The meaning of "lake bottom" may be a bit vague unless qualified by such terms as *original, false, exposed, recession, dry* and other attributives. An *original* bottom is that of the pristine lake before any lacustrine deposition. In later stages the "bottom" may be composed of lacustrine deposition, and it is "bottom" when it is sufficiently firm to stop the downward movement of some sounding weight in contrast to a "false bottom" through which the weight continues to fall. However, all degrees of firmness or penetrability may be found from "soup" to hard rock. The bed of an extinct lake, or one recently exposed by lake recession, or by drainage, may still be casually referred to as "lake bottom" although obviously no water covering is present.

See: *bed* (lake)
false bottom
floor (of a lake)

bottom gradient

See: *slope of basin*

bottom land, lake (mineral rights)

When an oil or gas field is developed under a lake bottom, the royalty percentage of a riparian is determined by his percentage of ownership of shoreline. If the riparian owns 1% of the shoreline, he is usually entitled to 1% of the bottomland royalties. The specific location of his land can be determined only by complete agreement of all riparians. Some states still retain all rights, title and interest in bottom lands.

See: *reliction* (lake land)

   submerged land (inland lakes)

bottom litter

Skin divers and scuba divers have noted the negative impact of underwater litter upon full enjoyment of their sport. Filter tips from cigarettes, cans, bottles, paper and plastic wrapping effectively destroy the aesthetic value of lake bottoms.

boulder pavement (of a lake)

In the process of wave erosion and cliff formation on a lake shore, the coarser matter of parent material such as glacial drift may remain as a residuum while the finer matter is carried away by waves and currents. In places the boulders and cobbles are compressed into the lake bottom and leveled off by ice pressure and wave action in a relatively smooth floor or pavement.

Boulder pavement exposed by low water level.

boundary lake

A lake on a boundary, or one crossed by a boundary line between two states or nations. On such lakes conflicts may arise over control and use of the waters and application of local laws, because of the separate jurisdictions. Lakes may also occur on the boundaries between minor political units such as counties and townships, and in such instances purely local conflicts in authority may arise.

The International Boundary between United States and Canada through Rainy Lake is permanently marked by numbered navigation pylons. Boaters on this lake may easily locate themselves by identifying the pylon number on their lake chart.

bowling alley

Prior to the development of more restrictive laws governing platting, lake lots often extended from the water line back to the boundary of the tract being subdivided. A fifty-foot lake lot could extend inland as much as 600 to 1,000 feet. Such lots are sometimes referred to as "bowling alleys" because of their long narrow shape.

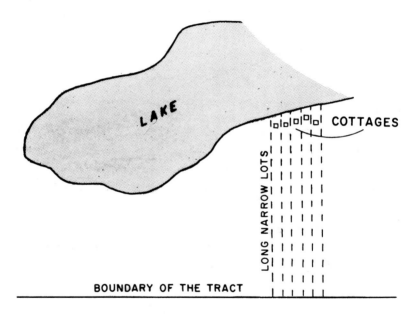

brackish water lakes, ponds

Along the sea coasts, in the marshes and swamps, containing lakes, ponds, sloughs, bayous, and channels; in the lagoons lying back of barrier beaches; in the estuaries and inlets the waters range from fresh to those with a salinity in excess of that of sea water. Commonly when these waters are slightly salty they are called "brackish". However, the term *brackish* may also be applied to the whole range of salinity between fresh water and that of sea water. The salinity of sea water is as an average about 3.5 percent.

Inland, especially in arid and semi-arid regions, *brackish* is also applied to waters of lakes and ponds, although it has no generally accepted precise meaning. Any distinction on a quantitative basis between *fresh* and *brackish* is arbitrary. The figures .02% and .05% have been used as limits for total salinity of *fresh* water; arbitrarily, water with more than .02% or .05% ceases to be fresh water.

See: *brine lakes*
salinity

brake

This term usually refers to a vegetational feature such as the *cane brakes* and *cypress brakes* of the Southern states, but in some locations such features are covered with water and therefore qualify as standing water bodies.

breadth (of a lake)

The length of a line from shore to shore cutting the line defining length at right angles at any point x.

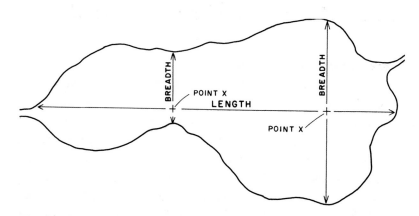

breaker line

The line where waves break as they approach the shore.

See: *plunge point*

breakwater

A structure for breaking the force of waves to protect craft anchored in a harbor; or to protect a beach from erosion.

An offshore barrier constituting a breakwater may be either an artificial structure or a natural formation. Sometimes it is connected at one, or both ends, with the shore.

brine lakes

In arid regions the waters in lakes in closed basins may become highly mineralized because the rate of evaporation is extremely high in relation to the input of fresh water. In time the total solids in solution may be in excess and often several times that of sea water. Such lakes are called *brine lakes*. The principal compound in solution may be salt ($Na\ Cl$) as in Great Salt Lake, sulfates of magnesium sulfates and carbonates of sodium and potassium. Where volcanic rocks are present in the watershed, borates may be present in the brines.

broken shoreline

One characterized by a large number of closely spaced islands, peninsulas, or jutting headlands.

buffalo wallows

A term popularly given to small, subcircular, shallow depressions which were once common throughout the Great Plains Region of Western U. S. They held water after rains, often remaining as stagnant water holes for a large part of the year. Buffalo visited them for water, trampled, wallowed in them for mud, and modified them, but were not the initial cause for the depressions. The term *buffalo wallows* has also been applied, (but improperly) to much larger natural depressions, many of which contain intermittent ponds or temporary lakes, which are widely distributed throughout this region especially on the High Plains.

bulkhead

A low wall of stones, concrete or piling built to protect a shore, or fills, from wave erosion. A bulkhead may be built to protect navigable waters, and serve as a line, limiting filling, or beyond which filling of submerged lands is not permitted.

bulkhead line

See: *bulkhead*

bulrush

(See illustration on page 50.)

This popular plant name is given to several species of *Scirpus* without discrimination. Some of the species often grow abundantly in nearly pure communities, covering wide areas, in shallow waters of lakes. These emergent aquatics often make a picturesque lakescape, and in some lakes slow the force of waves and thus have a shelter effect.

See: *rush lakes*
    shelter lakes

buoy

A prominently marked floating object that is anchored to the bottom to limit or guide watercraft and to mark swimming areas. Buoys may also be equipped with lights, bells and other warning systems.

Characteristic growth of bulrush in a lake. Photo — Pirnie, M.D., *Michigan Waterfowl Management,* Michigan Department of Conservation, 1935.

button bush ponds

Small ponds, usually no more than an acre or two in size, occupying closed basins. The ponds are characterized by a border zone of the shrub, *Cephalanthus occidentalis,*

which extends to the mean water line. The water is
shallow, usually partly filled with vegetation and stagnant. The button bush ponds, as described, are widely
distributed and numerous in the southern part of the
lower peninsula of Michigan.

caldera lake

A lake in a basin made by the subsidence of the cone
of a volcano. Crater Lake, Oregon is an example of a
caldera lake.

See: *crater lake*

camp scar (shore)

Camp sites on wilderness or primitive lakes are easily
recognized from the water surface and air by their lighter

Camp scar. Tofte Lake, Boundary Waters Canoe Area, Minnesota.

tone and barren character. Landing beaches are cleared, ground cover is destroyed and large trees are dead or dying from soil compaction.

Damage to the aesthetic image is frequently accentuated by blazes, temporary structures, fires and bark stripping.

canal, boat

A dredged canal through a marsh, or connecting two separate lakes, parts of a lake or a lake and a stream to provide convenient boat passage.

Boat canal through a marsh. Photo — Pirnie, M. D., *Michigan Waterfowl Management*, Michigan Department of Conservation, 1935 (photo by Walter E. Hastings).

canalized subdivision

A term for a lake subdivision which employs a system of canals to provide water access for back lots.

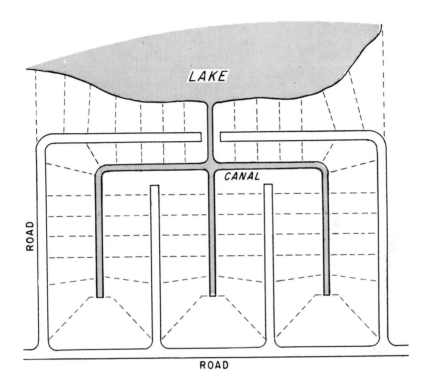

canoe ferry

A motorized boat, equipped with racks to carry canoes across large lakes.

canoe tow service

Tow service is available in canoe country for those people who desire assistance in crossing large lakes. The operator of the tow boat may tow a string of loaded canoes

Canoe ferry on a Northern Minnesota lake.

Canoe tow service on a large Boundary Waters Canoe Area lake.

canoe trail

Connected lakes or closely associated lakes and streams used as canoe routes. Portages used in overland travel between water bodies and camp sites may be either unmarked or developed; (1) wilderness area canoe routes are long and provide no facilities, (2) primitive area canoe routes are of variable length and have developed portages and camp sites, (3) canoe routes in populated agricultural and forest areas may be quite short and have hotels, organized campgrounds and pick-up service.

capacity-inflow ratio

The storage capacity of a reservoir or lake expressed as a ratio to the annual inflow.

cape (lake shore)

A rounded projection, out into the water, and either high land or low land. For inland lakes, *cape* rarely appears on maps as a place name and also only infrequently in descriptions. *Point* and *head* according to present usage appears to be preferred to *cape.*

carp mumblings

Minute depressions about one-quarter inch deep, in the soft, mud bottoms of lakes made by carp feeding on the bottom. Carp can completely destroy rooted submerged vegetation, increase turbidity and make the environment of a lake unsuitable for game fish.

carrying capacity (biologic)

The carrying capacity of a lake refers to its natural productivity. In relation to fish production, or other aquatic life, the numbers which the natural food supply, or pasturage, will support adequately.

carrying capacity (recreational)

The measure of the capacity of a lake for boating, skiing, bathing — recreational use in general — and residential occupation of the shore and shore border land without patent overcrowding, pollution and consequent danger to health and safety. Carrying capacity may be greatly limited if a single use is given priority; also it may be expanded if the surface area of the lake is zoned for particular uses and the time for use in each zone is specified.

Physical factors considered in determining the carrying capacity of a lake for a particular use, or combination of uses:

1. Size of lake and area of open water.
2. Depth and temperature of water.
3. Regularity or irregularity of the shoreline.
4. Islands, *blind islands*, obstructions at shallow depth; weed beds.
5. Width of beach; width of littoral shelf and its gradient.
6. Amount of water circulation and wave action.

Even though these factors are considered they cannot be given precise mathematical values. Size, or area alone is not the major determining factor. Where a lake is subject to wide fluctuations in level, a corresponding difference in its carrying capacity exists.

Other factors:

1. Regulatory and zoning restrictions.
2. Time; season of the year.

3. Accessibility; public or private.
4. Available services.
5. Level of pollution or smirchment.
6. Parking facilities.
7. Usable frontage.
8. Fish; abundance and species.

When is a lake overused? From the point of view of a riparian who seeks peace and quiet, a hundred people using the lake is overuse. From the point of view of a public park official a thousand might not be overuse.

See: *over-developed lake*
space consumption

carrying places

Land portaged in navigation of lakes and streams, and legally a part of the navigation route.

cat ice

"Ice forming a thin shell from under which the water has receded". (Navigation Dictionary USHO, Bulletin 220, 1956) The term has some application to ice on lakes.

cat-tail

The popular name for the species of *Typha* (*T. latifolia* and *T. angustifolia*), tall emergent aquatic plants, characterized by long flat leaves and a closed cylindrical spike at the end of the plant stem. The plants are common in marshes, the shallow marginal waters of lakes, and in shallow ponds. They are important feeding grounds in the production of muskrats and also furnish habitat for other aquatic animals and plants. Under some circumstances individual plants and extensive marshes have an aesthetic appeal.

Photo — Michigan Department of Conservation

Cattail contributes to winter aesthetics.

catchment basin

The entire area from which drainage is received by a river or a lake; most generally used in reference to surface runoff.

See: *hydrographic basin*
watershed

cathole

A localism used by early settlers in southern Michigan for very small (usually less than an acre) shallow depressions or *holes*. The name presumably originated from the characteristic aquatic plant, the cattail, (*Typha spp*). Later, the term came to be applied loosely to any shallow boggy or miry depression especially in the till clay plains. These depressions represented minor inequalities in the land surface left by the ice sheet and were originally numerous but have been largely obliterated by land clearing and land drainage. The term *cathole* is also an old colloquialism for a *hole* or pond, in a stream, or swamp, frequented by catfish.

causeway

A raised way or road made across wet or marshy ground or across the surface of a lake from shore to shore or from shore to an island. A causeway may be either a solid fill or an open structure.

cave-in lakes

See: *Kettle lakes; sink lakes; thaw lakes; thermokarst.*

center (of a lake)

The center may be regarded as a *point*, a *middle*, or a *median line*. If the shoreline of a lake made a perfect circle, the location of the center as a point would be a simple mathematical task. However, as lakes become more irregular in shape the task becomes more complicated, so that if a center as a point is established it can only be done in some *arbitrary* manner. "Middle" may be a vague undefined center, or a central area, or if definite, the "middle" is the median line. The median line of a lake, is the line all points of which are equally distant from the nearest points on opposite shores. Again, as lakes become more irregular in shape, the task of locating the median line becomes more complicated and arbitrary. Given a very irregular shore line, with a large number of riparian owners, a literal extension of individual property lines from the shore to a mathematical center point, or to a median line would pretty likely result in absurdities. Assuming that the determination of individual riparian property limits to the ultimate can become a legal necessity, a logical solution of the problem appears to be: separation of a compound lake into its natural segments, followed by a determination of the "middle" for each segment.

cesspool

Originally the term cesspool applied to the structure designed to hold sewage from a residence, more recently cesspool is used as a dramatic derogatory term to describe a lake which has been befouled by raw sewage or sewage treatment effluent.

chain of lakes

A local group consisting of a relatively small number of lakes tied together by live connecting streams or natural channels. The lakes are not restricted to any definite pattern of arrangement, or uniformity in size and spacing.

See: *gang of lakes*
swarm of lakes
train of lakes

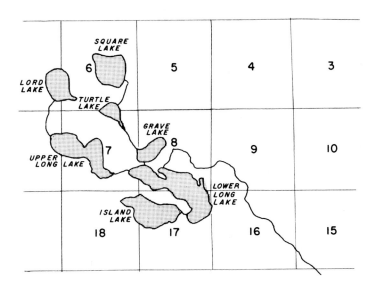

Chain of lakes, T2N, R10E, Oakland County, Michigan.

channel (lake)

In instances sub-lacustrine channels appear where a lake has been formed by the submergence of a valley, or the drowning of a river; the channels formed under sub-aerial conditions by stream cutting may remain unfilled by sediments, on the lake bottom. *Channel* is applied to navigable water within a lake such as a passage between islands, or other obstructions; and sometimes to a wide stretch in the nature of a strait, between an island and the mainland; a surface water way, either natural or artificial, which connects two lakes and provides for boat travel; to river distributaries and connecting waters in a delta; and to trench-like excavations extended inland from a lake shoreline to provide water frontage and boat access for back lots.

channel (lake basin)

The deeper, narrow elongated or more sharply trenched part of a lake bottom.

Chara

A genus of aquatic plants belonging to the Algae. The plants are characterized by a rough harsh stem, often encrusted with lime, cylindrical whorled branches at intervals

Dry Chara, exposed by a drop in lake level, appears white in the photo.

on the stem, and a strong musky odor. They are common as a submerged aquatic, loosely attached to the lake bottom soil, in practically all of the hardwater lakes of Michigan. The plants grow in both shallow and deep water (to depths of 15 to as much as 30 feet) and although they may furnish food and shelter for fish, they often attain such prolific growth that they become obnoxious and a nuisance. Most marl deposits in lake bottoms are believed to be composed mainly of the remains of Chara. Also known as *muskgrass* and *stonewort*.

charco

A pool, pond, or puddle. A pool in the bed of a stream, or a puddle in a playa flat. Limited in usage to Southwestern U. S.

An artificial *charco* does not have a dam and thus differs from a *tank* or *pond* which impounds run-off or stream water because of the construction of a dam.

chemical oxygen demand

Total oxygen consumed by the chemical oxidation of material in water.

In the potassium dichromate test, the total amount of oxidizable organic material in water is accepted as being proportional to the amount of potassium chromate used. This test is a more rapid test than that used for BOD. In case the water also contains toxic substances, this is the only test available for the determination of the organic load. The potassium dichromate test may also be accepted as being equivalent to the 20-day BOD test.

chemocline

The *chemocline* may be defined as the boundary between the *mixolimnion* and *monimolimnion*. The density gradient of a lake.

chilile

Inshore lake bottom. (Klugh, Ecology, Vol. IV, 1923, page 372)

chimney

An angular columnar mass of rock projecting from the water near shore. Such islands have been cut off from narrow rock headlands by wave erosion.

cienega (cienaga, cieneguita)

A word of Spanish origin. It appears in the Southwestern U. S. as a name for a seepage spot or place wet from springs, but also for a large marshy area which may contain standing water.

cirque lake

A lake occupying a rock basin usually at the head of a valley in high mountain ranges. A cirque is an amphitheater-like basin hollowed out of rock by glacial corrasion, or formed by other processes in which snow and ice and frost action are involved.

clay (lake bottom)

Clay in a mineralogic sense, namely various hydrous silicates of alumina, appears on lake bottoms as sediments, and sometimes constitute the original bottom or floor of lake basins and is relatively hard. It may be called "mud" when it is in a soft condition in the nature of ooze; when it is in recently exposed lake bottoms; and when it is trampled or wallowed in by animals. However the descriptive word "mud" is equally applied to fine textured bottom deposits which are mainly, or entirely, organic in composition.

clayballs

Both small and fairly large chunks of clay rounded by wave action. These are occasionally observed on Lake Michigan beaches, especially a narrow strand bordered by steep clay banks of hard glacial till. Also known as mud balls, armored mud balls, pudding balls. Balls of a different origin, aggregates from clay in suspension or in a viscous state, are also sometimes formed in the beds of lakes and rivers.

claybanks (lakeshore)

As a localism in Michigan, the term *claybanks* is applied to lake bluffs, or cliffs, composed almost entirely of till clay or glacial lacustrine clay; this regardless of height whether a few feet or more than a hundred feet.

cleanup program (lakeshore)

Lakeshore cleanup programs are most frequently organized as voluntary local beautification projects. Older lake communities begin to appear shabby due to lack of maintenance and abandonment of equipment and structures. Public spirited and enlightened individuals organize the program to enhance the lakeshore and restore the reputation of the community.

clear lakes

The term *clear* often appears in lake names and descriptions. It usually implies a high degree of transparency or low turbidity in the water. However, the terms "clear" and "crystal" are often used loosely and applied to lakes that are frequently "murky", or are transparent only to very shallow depths.

See: *transparency*

cliff (lakeshore)

The term *cliff* is often used interchangeably with *bank* and *bluff*, but in technical descriptions *cliff* is preferred for the wave-cut nearly vertical acclivity or abrupt slope which borders the waterline, or marks the position of the present or former shorelines of lakes. *Cliff* is applied regardless of the height of the feature, or of its rock composition, either hard rock or soft material.

Photo – U. S. Forest Service

Rock cliff, Lac La Croix, Minnesota.

closed lakes

Those that do not have an effluent in contrast to *drainage* lakes or *open* lakes which do have outlet streams.

Closed lakes are common in arid and semi-arid regions where they usually contain saline or brackish water.

> See: *blind lake*
> *enclosed lakes*
> *landlocked lake*

coast

According to prevailing usage the term is applied to land bordering seas. The shorelands of the Great Lakes are also called coasts, but the use of the term for the shoreland of small inland lakes appears to be quite inappropriate.

cobblestone pavement

> See: *boulder pavement*

C.O.D.

Abreviation for chemical oxygen demand.

> See: *chemical oxygen demand*

coliform bacteria

Coliform bacteria were formerly designated at the "*B. coli group*" and later as the "*coli aerogenes* group".

A test for coliform bacteria is commonly used to determine the presence of fecal coli from sewage. This group of coliform bacteria includes the facultative anaerobic, Gram-negative, rod-shaped cells and nonspore-forming bacteria which ferment lactose with gas formation within 48 hours of incubation at a temperature of 35 degrees centigrade.

A positive test would be accepted as an indicator of gross fecal pollution. Additional tests for pathogenic bacteria are less frequently used because these bacteria are present in very small numbers and disappear rather quickly due to their intolerance to natural surface water environment.

color (of lake waters)

Color is an effect of light penetration, radiation absorption and reflection; and is related to: transparency and depth of water; kind of lake bottoms and kind of matter held in solution; suspension or floating. Blues and greens are commonly observed in clear water lakes with clean bottoms of sand, rock or marl. Often the blue tints are in the deeper water and the greens in the shallower parts. Greens are often due to large populations of blue green and green algae in suspension or on the lake bottom. Yellows may be due to certain species of algae and to diatoms in large populations, and in certain types of lakes yellows have been attributed to sulfur bacteria. Pale yellows, yellow brown and coffee color or "black", can be produced by large quantities of dissolved humic substances and by particulate organic matter in suspension. Reds may be a reflection of the pigment color of certain algae; and may be caused by the presence of certain microcrustaceans and other zooplankton; the "blood lakes" of central Europe are attributed to presence of the microorganism *Euglena sanguinea*. Lake waters may be variously colored by suspended particulate inorganic matter especially that which is clayey or colloidal in nature. Some glacial lakes may be milky because of "glacial flour" in suspension, and the shallow water of marl lakes is often milky. Some colors are reflections of yellow sands on shallow bottoms, or from the black of organic sediments; or the blue of the sky. Colors vary with the weather, the time of day and the season.

The words *white* and *black* have been used to describe lake waters. *White* has been applied where the water is merely colorless, and sometimes where it is *milky* from gray or white particulate matter in suspension. *Black* may be due to: a large amount of humic matter in solution, such as that in water flowing from some kinds of bogs; reflection of black bottoms; the dull appearance of some waters when the sky is heavily overcast.

Unusual colors may be produced by pollution from industrial wastes.

commercial frontage (lake)

When riparian lands are zoned on the larger lakes, specific tracts are sometimes designated as commercial frontage, that is for business.

community beach

A beach dedicated for the semi-exclusive use of a definite subdivision. All the property owners in the subdivision may use the beach but others are excluded. This riparian right should be properly defined on the deed of each lot. The actual ownership of the community beach may be vested in an association or each separate lot owner may be vested with a riparian interest.

conductance tests

Electrical measurements, based on the conductivity of the water, which reflect the total concentration of electrolytes, in solution. The tests are used to determine whether variations, with time and other circumstances, exist in the concentration of matter in solution; as a check on results obtained by other analytic methods; and sometimes are interpreted as a measure of the fertility of the water.

conflicting uses (of lake)

Uses by certain riparians that act to the detriment of other riparian users. It appears that the injury resulting from a particular use may be real or just an assumed threat. Technically, conflicts of use may exist only between riparians because all acts of others would be in the realm of trespass.

Photo – Michigan Department of Conservation

Conflict between two water uses.

Examples of conflicting uses:

    Fishing vs waterskiing
    Boating vs swimming
    Boating vs canoeing
    Fishing vs duck hunting
    Aquatic weed control vs fishing and hunting
    Lake aesthetics vs intensive lake use
    Dredging and filling vs fishing and hunting
    Public access use vs private riparians

connecting stream

A stream connecting a lake with another lake or with a river.

See: *necfluve*

consequent island

An original island. An elevation in the lake basin which remained above the water surface at the time of the formation of the lake. Also called residual island.

consequent lakes

Lakes existing in depressions which represent the original inequalities in a new land surface. The ponds and lakes in depressions on the recently uplifted plains of sedimentation bordering the Atlantic Coast and forming a part of the Coastal Plain of the Southeastern U. S. are *consequent.* Also called *newland lakes,* by W. H. Hobbs. Lakes in a plain of glacial deposition may also be *consequent.*

consumptive waste (water)

Water that is consumed by plants without any economic benefit to man.

contamination (lake)
　　See: *pollution*

control structure (lake level)
　　A dam, dike, pump or any structure built for the purpose of controlling the water level of a lake or pond.

cooling water
　　Water that has been used primarily for cooling in an
industrial or manufacturing process. In the disposal of
cooling water, its temperature is normally higher than
that of a lake or stream receiving it and under some circumstances it can be regarded as *pollution* or *smirchment*.

correlative rights doctrine
　　Where a source of water does not provide enough for
all users, the water is reapportioned proportionately on
the basis of prior water rights held by each user.

cottage (lake)
　　A relatively small seasonal, or year round, structure on
a lake shore, or on a lot adjacent to and with access to a
lake. The "cottage" serves a recreational purpose. It may
be a structure scantily constructed and furnished, or may
be one as substantially built and equipped as an urban
residence.
　　　　See: *amphibian cottage*
　　　　　　hanging cottage
　　　　　　pile dwellings

cottage setback
　　Property deeds sometimes include clauses establishing
a minimum setback for future structures. For example,
no structure except a dock or boathouse may be built less
than fifty feet from the waterline.

cottage-water ratio

The ratio between the number of shoreland cottages
or lake homes (whose owners or occupants have access to
the water) and the area (expressed in acres) of the lake
surface.

cove

In usage, the term is occasionally applied both to
narrow recesses and to fairly broad looped embayments of
the shorelines of inland lakes; not consistently distinguished
from bay.

cranberry bog

Native cranberries have been commercially harvested
from natural bogs in Michigan and other States. Most
commercial operations require planting and some form of
water level control for frost protection and to facilitate
harvesting.

crannog

A lake dwelling. (Scotland and Ireland) The word
could be appropriated, and become useful in the vocabulary of *Lacology*, if extended in meaning to apply to a
dwelling built offshore in a lake, and designed as a retreat,
for privacy or seclusion.

crater lake

A lake formed in the crater of a volcano. *Caldera* are
basins formed by the collapse of magma in the vents of
volcanoes. *Maars* are basins formed by single explosive
eruptions. Depressions in the earth's surface made by impact of falling meteors are also called *craters*, although
the existence of only a few crater lakes of this origin has
been clearly established.

cryolimnon

A proposed term for a body of open water in a nearly completely frozen over, or ice covered, inland lake. On

Open water "cryolimnon" in a frozen over lake.

some lakes the open water may represent either the location of the deeper holes in the basin; or the location of springs on the bottom or shore.

cryptodepressions (lakes)

Lake basins whose deep parts are below sea level.

culvert dam

When culverts are constructed under roads that cross over the effluent stream (outlet) of a lake, they may be laid at a level higher than the original stream bed. When

Road culvert replacing the natural outlet of a lake.

installed in this fashion they act as low head dams and may raise the level of the entire lake. The culvert acts as an outlet when the water rises to its level.

current canal (through weed bed)

The continuous current caused by an influent (inlet) or effluent (outlet) stream may effectively limit the growth of aquatic plants and create canal like openings through weed beds.

currents (lake)

Movements or flows of the water. The water may be set in motion by the effects of winds and waves, by difference in temperature and density and by gravity. Currents of various kinds and names have been recognized: littoral; longshore; undertow; rip; density; convection; turbidity; eddies; stream.

cuspate foreland

Two spits developed from the shore join in a point out in the lake to form a V-bar and a foreland. The space between the enclosing sides may be water; or the foreland may be a complex of beach deposits cuspate in form. A cuspate foreland is produced by the formation of successive cuspate bars farther and farther seaward.

cusps

Triangular deposits of sand, or other current drift, spaced along a shore. The point of the triangle is out in the water and the base on the shore. Their size and configuration is apparently controlled by the magnitude and direction of wave action or current forces. Cusps under some conditions are transient, formed by storm waves and erased by a succeeding storm, but under other conditions are fairly long and relatively permanent features.

As cusps are designated on maps and photographs, the distinction between a *spit* and a *cusp* often becomes a bit blurred. Some *cusps* are *spits* that are cuspate in form. The spit may be recurved — a hook; the cusp ends in a straight point.

See: *spit*

cut and built terrace
> See: *littoral shelf*
> *wave built terrace*

cypress ponds
In some of the Southern states of the U. S., especially Florida, some ponds, or lakes, are characterized by a growth of cypress (*Taxodium spp*). The growth may be sparse, or the ponds may be so full of trees that it is difficult to use a boat on them.

cypriere
In Louisiana, a cypress swamp. Cypress swamps generally are permanently water covered areas.

dam
An engineering structure, or man-made feature of any kind, designed to hold back a flow of water and create an impoundment, or raise the level of a pre-existing body of water. Dam may be used in a figurative sense for a body of standing water. Where DAM is a place name, the name usually implies the impoundment of water as well as the engineering structure. Impoundments may be formed by natural dams, such as those by lodgment of driftwood across a stream channel, by alluvial deposition, by landslides, and those made by the beaver.

dam lake
One created by a dam. The term is usually applied to a water body formed back of a man-made dam.

dam pond
An impoundment back of a man-made dam. It is not restricted in size, and can be the equivalent of *reservoir,*

lake, basin and *backwater*. In some locations *dam pond* is the generic in the place name of the water body.

daughter lake

An imaginative name for a small lake which was once a part of a larger body of water, but from which it has been detached or separated by natural processes. For example, the daughter lake may represent the water of a bay, or arm, which has been cut off from the main body of the lake by natural filling. The separate water body remains very closely adjoining the larger lake, or may be connected with it by a channel. This term was used by C. A. Davis in the description of lakes in the volume on Marl (Bog-Lime), published by the Michigan Geological Survey, 1903, but subsequent instances of its use have been few. Frequently a channel is dredged to connect the "daughter lake" to the larger body of water.

dead beaver lodge

An abandoned beaver lodge.

dead end lake access

The right of ways of many public roads terminate at the shorelines of lakes. These roads are frequently used to gain access to the lake although the space is limited. The legality of this use is frequently questioned.

dead lakes

Colloquialism sometimes applied to lakes that have become filled with vegetation and therefore present a stagnant condition.

The terms *senescent, dying* and *dead* are often applied to lakes indiscriminately.

See: *extinction*
senescent lake

dead sea

As applied to lakes, a calm condition of the water surface, as opposed to a surface characterized by waves.

deadhead

A log lying on the bottom of a lake, or in the bed of a river. Often a boating hazard.

See: *snag lake*

deadwater

An appropriate term for stream water which has had its flow so slackened by dams or other causes that it appears to be "still" or "dead".

deed restrictions (lake lot)

In the shoreland development of a private lake, lot deeds may carry restrictions usually found in city zoning ordinances pertaining to size and type of construction, setback, right of ways for services, sewage disposal, signs, fences, commercial uses, rubbish disposal, landscape work, sale of property and also restrictions upon use of the lake by the lot owner. These latter restrictions could limit or restrict any water use such as fishing, hunting, and diversion of water.

When properly incorporated and administered, deed restrictions may have the same desirable effect as zoning restrictions.

deeps (of lakes)

The holes, trenches, or the more profound depressions in the floors or bottoms of lakes occupying compound basins.

deflation lakes

Lakes, ponds, or pools occupying basins formed mainly by wind erosion. These are most common in arid or semi-arid regions and here are mostly intermittent. Ponds or small lakes occur in blow outs in dune areas in addition to those water bodies occupying the deeper valley depressions or hollows which are enclosed by parallel dune ridges. Blow out and deflation ponds occur in areas of shifting dunes and on wind swept sand flats bordering the eastern shoreline of Lake Michigan.

delta lakes

A river flowing into a lake, estuary, or coastal bay deposits its load of sediment and finally builds the deposit above water level, usually in a delta form. With continued deposition the delta advances into the open water usually with an irregular or ragged front, and the bays of water in the front are often enclosed by bar deposition and other processes thus producing delta lakes. In some deltas the main stream may split up into a large number of distributaries or separate channels. Sloughs and bayous are also characteristic features of deltas.

density currents

Inflowing water, especially if turbid, or laden with sediment, may be denser than the surface lake water, and therefore sinks and creates a *density current*. Denser water may sink to the bottom of the lake, or may sink until it reaches a layer of water of greater density, and thence moves horizontally. When the inflowing water is lesser in density, it flows over the surface water of the lake. The density of water is increased by material in solution or suspension and by lowering its summer temperature.

See: *fall overturn*
spring overturn

depth (of lakes)

Thickness of the water; unless otherwise indicated depth generally implies the whole vertical distance between the surface, at a known position on the lake, and the lake bottom.

Depth figures are recognized as essential data in limnological, ecological and hydrologic studies; and depth is a basic factor in the evaluation of a body of standing water as a natural resource. However, depth of a lake is something that cannot be obtained with any great mathematical precision. The figures reported for depths, from different sources, in particular maximum depth, for inland lakes often show considerable disagreement. The causes for discrepancies and lack of precision are: (1) in a compound basin of a large lake deep holes are easily missed in random soundings, and often in organized lake surveys, but are subsequently discovered and reported; (2) some lakes are subject to considerable fluctuations in level, so that a depth reported at one time may be different from that of another time for the same location; (3) the determination of the lake bottoms is sometimes arbitrary where a thick deposit of soft matter, or a false bottom, occurs; (4) different methods of making soundings and procedures in recording depth measurements do not always yield the same results.

In lake descriptions, it is not uncommon for the writer to state the depth as "reported" without citing any authority. Such "reported" depths are often found to be widely in error.

depth — area ratio

The area of a lake, by depth classification, expressed as a ratio to the total lake area.

Example:
  Lake area = 100 acres
  Area in 0-6 foot depth classification = 10 acres
  Depth - area ratio of 0-6 foot depth = 1:10

desiccation (of lakes)

Loss of water by direct evaporation. *Desiccation* usually implies thorough dryness of the whole lake bed area. Siccation of lakes may result primarily from other causes than desiccation or evaporation. Other causes are: (1) drainage by cutting outlets or by dredging natural outlet streams; (2) escape of water through opening of subterranean outlets; (3) drop in the level of the ground water table; (4) removal or destruction of dams.

See: *lake regimen*

destratification of a lake

Artificial circulation or mixing of the water. A device using compressed air may be used to force the cold stagnant water of the hypolimnion up through the thermocline thus mixing it with the warmer oxygenated water of the epilimnion.

detention reservoir

A basin (above a dam) constructed for the temporary storage of streamflow and superficial surface run-off. Also called retarding reservoir.

detergents, synthetic (in lake waters)

Introduced into lake water mainly from raw sewage and in the effluents of sewage treatment plants and from septic tanks. Detergents reduce the uptake of oxygen at the water surface; and are a cause of foaming in water (often an indication of pollution), and a source of foam streaks.

Pollution from this cause may be greatly lessened by the use of new detergents that are more rapidly decomposable.

developed shore (economic)
Shore land that has been occupied by man, or modified for his use. The "development" may take the form of buildings for residential use, resorts, commercial structures, or improvements for recreational purposes.
See: *shoreline acreage ratio*
shoreline development ratio

development costs (lake lots)
The costs normally involved in the development and sale of riparian frontage. If a person purchases undeveloped land on a lake, subject to future payment of development costs, he could expect to pay for all development costs considered to be usual, necessary and convenient for that location.

development of lake shores (physiographic)
Modifications by physiographic or natural processes such as erosion of headlands resulting in smoothing the shoreline, and formation of beaches, bars, etc.

development of lakes (economic)
Modifications by man for private business or for public recreational purposes, such as the subdivision of shore land into lots, landscaping, filling, dredging, building of beaches, construction of access roads, etc. Development possesses a lake community connotation.

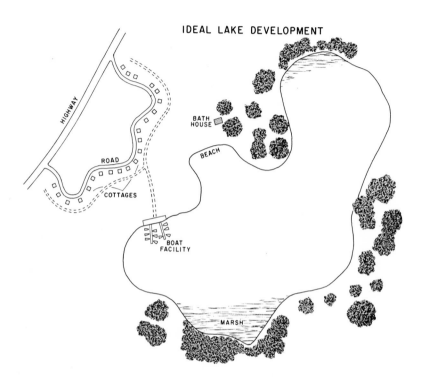

IDEAL LAKE DEVELOPMENT

Inland lakes are beautiful because of their unique physical characteristics. As soon as development starts, the physical beauty is changed. Trees on the shoreland are removed for cottages, land is graded for landscaping purposes and beaches are cleared. Soon, as development continues, the physical beauty is almost replaced by the symmetrical pattern of roads, structures and service features.

Would it be possible to use a lake without escalating it into the category of a metropolitan suburb?

The benefits available from systematic artistic planning would include economy, simplicity and the protection of the original shoreline beauty of the lake.

dew pond

In the chalk hills district of England, where potable water is difficult to obtain dew ponds are constructed to collect water by condensation. A natural depression or basin (200 to 400 feet in diameter) is covered with a thick layer of coarse rock or gravel. Building paper is laid over the gravel and a thick layer of concrete is poured over the entire basin except for the upper edge. In the evening, cooling of the concrete slab proceeds rapidly due to the gravel mulch and water from moist warm air condenses on the upper surface of the concrete and collects in the bottom of the dew pond. This water is utilized for household use and livestock.

Precipitation adds to the water collected in the dew pond. The cool surface of the water also provides a condensation surface.

Historically, dew ponds were constructed in the Sussex region of England by using a straw base for insulation and clay for surfacing. A thick layer of clay would serve as a condensation surface and would also hold the water collected.

diatoms

Microscopic plants which occur abundantly as floating forms in plankton. They sometimes occur abundantly enough to produce a water "bloom" and give a color tint yellowish or brownish, to the water. *Diatoms* are notable for their shells of silica, and the siliceous character imparted to bottom deposits by their remains.

diffused water

A legal term for vagrant water on the surface of land not yet in natural watercourses or lakes. It includes overland sheet runoff and temporary puddles, or plash, occurring after a rainstorm. Vagrant water collected and stored in artificial ponds or other enclosures becomes the property of the land owner. Diffused water has no precise meaning as a hydrogeologic term.

dike (dyke)

Dikes, artificial embankments (technically neither *dams* nor *levees*) have been constructed to hold bodies of water, mostly on relatively flat land. A body of water so retained may be in the nature of a reservoir, lake, pond or flooding. Also dikes may be constructed on the shores or borders of a lake either to prevent flooding, from overflow of the lake, of adjacent land, or to prevent inflow into a lake of undesirable water.

Dike also has the meaning of a ditch which holds water, but such usage is rare.

dipping

Drinking and cooking water is commonly dipped from a wilderness or primitive lake. It is usually suggested that the water be dipped from 18 inches below the surface out some distance from shallow water. (Note — this practice is not recommended by public health agencies, regardless of the location of the lake.)

disciplined waters

A shop term applied to a stream, or other waters, which has been modified by engineering measures and structures and thereby brought under control to a degree to make it better serve some particular use.

dismal

A term sometimes applied to fresh water swamps in eastern parts of the United States especially in the flat coastal plain region from Virginia southward.

disposal area, lake improvement

An area of land, usually in a marsh or swamp, where dredged material from a lake improvement project is deposited.

dissolved oxygen

The amount of dissolved oxygen in parts per million present in water. Oxygen available in water is a critical factor for fish and other organisms.

District (Lake)

A geographic region characterized by a large number of lakes. The region and lakes may have a general unity, such as geologic origin, although individual lakes, and minor groups, may differ markedly. The Lake District of western England is a famous example and in America the Quetico-Superior District of Minnesota and Ontario, Canada.

diversion of water (from a lake)

Draining, pumping, siphoning or removal of water from a lake in any manner that is not natural. It is assumed that diversion covers either the temporary or permanent removal of water.

diving raft

A floating structure anchored in deep water, used for diving and swimming.

Photo – Michigan Department of Conservation

Diving raft at top, right background.

D.O.

An abbreviation for dissolved oxygen.
See: *dissolved oxygen*

dock (inland lakes)

On inland lakes commonly applied to a structure, usually a narrow walk or platform of wood supported on posts or floats extending from the shore out into the lake for the purpose of anchorage and landing of boats. Ex-

A type of removable and adjustable dock.

ceptionally a dock or pier, may be a fill or solid structure. Also a dock may be extended out into deep water and be used as a diving platform. *Pier* and *dock* are used synonymously.

doline lake

A lake occupying a bowl or circular deepening re- sulting from solution of limestone by ground water at intersecting joint planes.

drag line

A machine sometimes used to remove bottom material from a lake. Basically it consists of a sturdy bucket which is pulled out into the water by an anchored cable or swung into the lake from a boom. When it is pulled back upon shore it fills with bottom material which is subsequently dumped on the shore.

drain

A surface ditch or underground tile line constructed for the purpose of lowering the water table so that land may be farmed or used for other purposes. The excess

Photo – Wisconsin Department of Conservation

Drain installed to lower lake level.

water is usually led to the nearest lower natural drainage way and released.

When a drain is located near a lake, to reclaim associated lowland, the water level of the lake may be lowered. In some locations, the entire lake may be drained in order to reclaim lake bottom for agricultural or other uses.

drainage lake

A lake which has an effluent; one whose level is largely controlled by the discharge of an outflowing stream. A *drainage lake* is opposed to a *closed lake* (which see).

In its usage in Wisconsin, *drainage lake* has been applied to those kettle hole, or pit lakes in moraines and outwash plains, which have inflowing and outflowing streams, in contrast to those in closed basins, where presumably water is lost through seepage.

See: *seepage lake*

drawdown

An engineering term for a decrease in the levels of reservoirs or other impoundments, caused by intensive use for hydroelectric power production, or to withdrawals made as a safety precaution against flooding or ice damage or for other management practices.

Drawdown on a reservoir.

A *drawdown*, because it lowers the water level, may create a conflict of interest between user groups.

drift

(1) Detrital material moved and deposited by currents, as *littoral drift*. (2) Floating material washed ashore and left stranded. (3) The speed of a current. (4) Glacial drift — deposits of various kinds, sands, gravels, boulders, clays, generally unconsolidated made by glaciers and glacio fluvial waters. Lakes in the glaciated regions of the

United States occupy basins composed of drift, or in some
other way related to the deposits of drift of the glacial
periods of the Pleistocene.

drift line

Floating material and other detritus washed ashore
and left stranded in a line. Drift lines mark the changes
in level from the high water line of a flood zone of a
reservoir; and the fluctuations in levels of a natural lake.

driftwood

In connection with lakes, commonly the term applies
to floatage consisting of parts of trees and other wood
fragments that have been cast ashore or lodged on beaches
by storm waves. Selected pieces of beach driftwood are
collected for recreation and as a hobby, and also are
collected for their artistic or money value when made into
decorative pieces and objects of art.

drinking water lakes

A descriptive phrase used in Canada for lakes which
are assumed to be pure enough to be suitable for drinking
water.

drop-off

See: *beach profile* for illustration

The scarp or bank of a sub-aqueous terrace or littoral
shelf. The place where a shoal bottom of a lake, or where
the gentle slope from a shore, drops suddenly into deep
water; also sometimes called "step off".

drowned valley lakes

The formation of lakes, usually at the mouths of rivers,
due to land subsidence and resulting inundation.

Submergence of coast land, causing the "drowning" of rivers at their mouths and the formation of estuaries has been pretty much restricted to sea-coasts, but a number of lakes, at the mouths of rivers entering Lake Michigan, on the east shore from Frankfort, Michigan southward, are attributed in origin to the "drowning" of the streams.

See: *ria lakes*

dry beach

See: *beach profile* for illustration

The area on a beach, above the water line, not covered by normal wave water. The "dry beach" however may be subject to action by storm waves.

See: *wet beach*

dry dam

A retarding structure, on a headwater stream, designed for flash flood control. Permanent storage is not involved and the bottom can be farmed or grazed between flood periods.

See: *drybed reservoir*

dry lakes

This term is applied to the sites of former lakes. In usage the bed of the former lake is not necessarily literally *dry*, but may support a marsh type of vegetation, or in the lower part of the basin even aquatic vegetation. The desiccation, or loss of surface water, is not due mainly to loss by evaporation, as in arid regions, but by drop in level of a local water table, filling by aquatic vegetation, or by land drainage operations.

A large number of basins which contained water during the early period of settlement were given geographic names as lakes, have lost their surface water permanently.

In some instances, however, they still retain the place name given to the original water area.

"Dry lakes," though intended mainly for those basins which have become desiccated more recently, could be extended to apply also to basins which lost their water, as a result of geologic processes, early in the evolution of the post-glacial landscape. In some of these, the original lake bottom contains no more moisture than the adjacent, normal, well-drained upland soil.

See: *desiccation*

drybed reservoir

A detention reservoir — one that does not contain water except in time of flood.

dual drainage lakes

Lakes that have two or more outlet streams that discharge water in opposite directions and into separate hydrographic basins. Such lakes are not common and where they do exist they are especially notable. Some lakes have achieved double outlets because of reversal of flow of influents from dams, river piracy, and other causes such as artificial drains. Some lakes have dual drainage intermittently, that is during high level periods or during seasons of heavy precipitation and some are quasi-dual such as those in lime sink basins that have surface outlets and also subterranean outlets.

duck blind (lake marsh)

A temporary or permanent structure camouflaged with cattail or other emergent vegetation to provide cover for wildfowl hunters.

duck-out ponds

A term which has been applied to dug-out ponds, or ranch ponds, used by wild ducks for short rest periods.

duck potato

Sagittaria latifolia; a small emergent aquatic plant, common in very shallow water near the shorelines of lakes. The plant, especially the tuber, furnishes food for ducks. Also called *wapato.*

duckweeds

Species of *Lemna, Spirodela* and *Wolffia.* Tiny floating plants which sometimes form a nearly complete cover on the surface of small still water lakes and ponds and on the water of sheltered bays of large lakes. The plants are a source of food for ducks and muskrats.

dugout pond

A pond, or reservoir, made by excavation, in contrast to one created by impoundment or construction of a dam. On range land in Western U. S. *dugout, waterhole, charco* and *tank* often mean the same thing.

dune shore

A shorezone characterized by wind-deposited sand derived from sand beaches. Lee slopes are normally steep (natural angle of repose for sand) and the windward slopes are more gentle. If the dunes are "active", the topography may be uneven and hummocky. Old dunes may be completely stabilized with forest cover.

dy

Lake bottom sediment consisting of unhumified, or peaty, organic matter such as that derived from an acid peat bog. The organic sediment of a dystrophic lake.

dying lake

(1) A colloquial term for a lake nearing extinction from any cause; (2) a *senescent* lake. The words *dead*, *dying*, and *senescent* as applied to lakes, are often used indiscriminately.

A lake nearing extinction by filling by aquatic vegetation.

dystrophic lakes

Those lakes associated with acid peat bogs, and largely filled with sediments consisting of unhumified or peaty organic matter. Typically the water is yellowish or brownish, low in calcium, often acid and low in fish productivity.

easement access

When access to a water body is obtained by easement, the riparian owner sells the right of access but retains ownership of the land.

economic classes of lakes and lakelands

When sufficient data are available covering lakes and lakeland development, these resources may be grouped into economic classes. Criteria for classification would consist of use, present type and intensity of development. This knowledge would be useful for the determination of realistic management programs designed to maximize use and to provide protection of investment and the resource.

Undeveloped lakes could also be classified in terms of their potential value and use, but far more information would be required: future demand for water; trends in recreational requirements; growth of public ownership and statutory controls; future construction of artificial lakes and streams; accessibility of lakes and streams of competitive recreational regions; and future control of *pollution* and *smirchment*.

LAKE AND LAKELAND – ECONOMIC CLASSES

I. Lake Water and Bottom Uses

A. Recreational

(a) Fishing
(1) Still fishing
(2) Casting
(3) Trolling
(4) Fly fishing
(5) Bow and arrow fishing
(6) Ice fishing
(7) Spearing

(b) Motor boating
(1) Pleasure cruising
(2) Water-skiing
(3) Surfing

(c) Rowboats
(d) Sailing
(e) Canoeing
(f) Iceboating
(g) Snow scooters and snow-mobiles
(h) Skating
(i) Beach sports
   (1) Swimming
   (2) Sunbathing
   (3) Wading
(j) Hunting and trapping
(k) Aesthetic recreational uses

B. Wildlife Refuge — Sanctuary
C. Industrial — Commercial

(a) Reservoirs (power plants); Mill Ponds
(b) Water Supply — Municipal, Domestic, Irrigation, Manufacturing
(c) Fish Production
(d) Trapping, Fericulture
(e) Aquatic Plant Production — Aquaponics
(f) Navigation
(g) Mining (marl, sand, gravel, salt, borax, potash, iron ore)
(h) Ice Harvesting
(i) Waste Disposal — Factory, Mine, Rubbish

II. Shoreland — Water Frontage

A. Undeveloped — Wild Land
B. Site Value; as an investment
C. Developed

(a) Cottages (seasonal, year round)
(b) Mixed Cottages, Resorts, Commercial Buildings
(c) Public Park

(d) Private Club
(e) Manufacturing Plants, Urban-Commercial Businesses, Marinas

III. Lake Vicinage

A. Wild Land
(a) Wooded; swamp and upland forest
(b) Treeless; marsh and bog

B. Rural Farm
C. Idle Cleared Land
D. Urban-Suburban
E. Rural Lake Community

edificarian environment

The kinds of buildings on the lake frontage and lake vicinage.

See: *environment* (lake)

effluent (lake)

See: *inlet* for illustration

A surface stream flowing out of a lake; an outlet stream, or outlet. In instances of lakes in a river flood plain, a stream which is normally an *effluent* may have its flow temporarily reversed because of pressure of back water, and thereby become an influent. Lakes have been observed which have more than one effluent.

A discharge stream may be intermittent in flow and still be an *effluent*, but the term is not a proper one for artificial outlets which are no more than drainage ditches, cuts, channels or canals.

See: *drainage lake*
inlet
outlet

effluent (pollution)

(1) The water discharged after use in the treatment of sewage; (2) water discharged from storm and sanitary sewers; (3) water discharged after the treatment of industrial products, or from tanks or containers after any use.

These effluents entering lakes are generally regarded as pollutants.

egress (lake)

Egress is legally restricted to the act of departing from a lake. Where public access to lake waters is provided, *egress* from the waters, by the public, is implied or stipulated in order to avoid trespass on private property.

See: *ingress*

embankments (lake)

Depositional features along shorelines, such as spits and bars.

embayment

A descriptive word for a recess in a shoreline. Rarely used in place names.

emergent aquatic plants

Rooted plants that grow in shallow water with a portion of their stems and leaves growing above the water surface, such as the bulrush *(Scirpus .spp)*, and cattail, *(Typha spp)*. Also called emersed aquatic plants.

enclosed lakes (or basins)

Lakes which have neither inflowing or outflowing streams, and those which never overflow the rims of their basins. The *enclosed* lake is distinguished from the *closed* lake because some kinds of the latter may have inflowing streams. Enclosed lakes may occur in hole-like depressions, and only partly fill them, such as sinkholes or solution depressions; kettles or potholes in glaciated regions; hollows in dune areas and other deflation depressions; craters in volcanic regions.

Lakes may be cited which have neither surface influents or affluents yet do not quite fit the concept of the enclosed lake. These *pseudo-enclosed* lakes occur as: remnants of larger lakes which are in a state of near extinction; as satellites closely adjoining larger lakes; rimless patches of open water in marshes, inside ponds of delta plains; and oxbow lakes of river flood plains. All of these either occur in open basins, have sub-surface connections with open lakes or streams, or are subject to flooding.

enriched lake

A lake that has received inputs of nitrates, phosphates and other nutrients, thereby greatly increasing the growth potential for algae and other aquatic plants. Most frequently, enrichment results from the inflow of sewage effluent but may sometimes be related to the movement of commercial agricultural fertilizer into the lake basin.

See: *eutrophication*

environment (lake)

(1) The total of natural conditions which exert an effect on the organisms of the lake; (2) in a sociologic and economic sense, the total of natural and artificial conditions of the lake and borderland, including the kind of occupancy, which has an influence upon human behavior, and upon economic values.

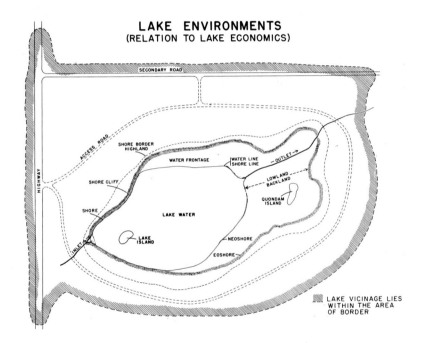

LAKE ENVIRONMENTS
(RELATION TO LAKE ECONOMICS)

eoshoreline

See: *beach profile* for illustration
environment for illustration

Old shoreline; shoreline features marking the water-line of former lake stages, which may be either higher (usually) or lower (rarely) than the existing water level.

ephemeral lakes, ponds

Short lived lakes and ponds. Examples: beach pools and lagoons; deflation lakes; ponds in dune hollows; water bodies in river flood plains left by one flood and destroyed by succeeding floods; some lime sink ponds that have intermittent subterranean outlets.

epilimnion

In a thermally stratified lake, the turbulent layer of water that extends from the surface to the *thermocline*.

equalizing reservoir

Banks Lake, a large irrigation reservoir in the Grand Coulee near the Grand Coulee Dam on the Columbia River in the State of Washington, is called an *equalizing reservoir*. During the season of abundance of flow, in the river, water is lifted at a pumping station at the Dam to a feeder canal in the Grand Coulee which fills the reservoir. The supply in Banks Lake thence makes it unnecessary to pump water for irrigation from the river in the spring and fall when the stage is low .

Escherichia coli

The group of bacteria known as *Escherichia coli* represent about 90% of the fecal coli discharged in sewage. If the coliform test of a lake water sample is positive, the presence of these bacteria should be suspected. Such water should not be used for drinking purposes unless treated.

See: *coliform bacteria*

esplanade

Much the same meaning as *promenade*.

See: *promenade*

estanque
>See: *tank*

eulittoral zone
The shore zone representing the limits of fluctuation in water level.
>See: *littoral*
>*profundal*
>*sublittoral*

euphotic zone
In lakes, the depth zone through which light penetrates, and is effective in photosynthesis. The zone beneath the euphotic is termed aphotic, a zone in which light penetration and oxygen production are insufficient to maintain productivity at compensation — the level at which respiration and decomposition consume oxygen at a rate equal to that at which oxygen is produced.

eutrophic lakes
"Rich" lakes; those well provided with the basic nutrients required for plant and animal production.

eutrophication (lake)
Enrichment of the water or lake soil. Increase in nutrients required for the growth of organisms may come about by natural processes; or rapid enrichment may take place due to some cause such as the introduction of sewage effluent.
>See: *enriched lake*

evanescent lakes
Depressions containing water for only a very short time after rains. Water is lost by rapid evaporation or by rapid seepage or by both.

Evanescent usually implies a shorter life than *ephemeral*, but often the two words have much the same meaning, namely short lived.

See: *ephemeral lakes*

evaporation loss

Water lost from a lake surface by combined effect of solar radiation and wind circulation. Evaporation losses may be as little as 24 inches but can be as high as 70 inches per year depending upon the climatic environment.

See: *sublimation losses*

evaporation suppression

Various fatty alcohols, which create mono-molecular films are in use in Australia and southwestern United States to reduce evaporation losses from reservoirs. Commonly, these materials are either frequently applied or constantly applied by distributors mounted on rafts.

Under laboratory conditions, evaporation may be decreased as much as 90% but under field conditions their efficiency is less. Use of mono-molecular films for evaporation suppression on several large reservoirs in southwestern United States has been determined to be successful on a cost-benefit basis.

evapotranspiration losses (lake)

The combined losses from a lake surface due to evaporation, sublimation and transpiration; exact measurements are extremely difficult. Commonly, evapotranspiration losses are stated as estimates.

See: *evaporation loss*
sublimation losses
transpiration losses

excavated reservoirs
Storage in basins made by excavation. Such "reservoirs" are usually small in size, and provide water for farm use.

exclusive riparian rights
Riparian rights that are owned or controlled by a single owner. For example, a hunting club owns all the hunting rights on a particular lake and therefore has the exclusive right to hunt; other riparians and the public cannot hunt on the lake.

Under the riparian doctrine a single riparian owner on a lake or stream has the exclusive right to the use of his beach, to ice and the bottomlands between his shoreline and the center, to minerals under his bottomlands, to anchorage rights on his bottomlands, to wharfage and dockage associated with his beach and bottomlands. Insofar as proprietary ownership applies, the riparian also owns the surface water, fish and game on and in the water overlying his bottomlands.

extinction (lake)
A lake is *extinct* when it has lost all of its water permanently; or when a surface exposure of the water in its basin no longer exists, or when its open water has been replaced by vegetation and has reached the status of a bog, marsh or swamp. An "extinct lake" may contain temporary, or ephemeral pools of water in its bed following periods of precipitation, and some bogs and marshes, which represent the sites of former lakes, may be permanently wetland. In some instances lakes may be alternately "dry" or have their basins full of water over considerable periods, and here a nice distinction between *extinction* and *intermittency*, or temporary extinction, may be difficult. Also whether a particular lake is actually

extinct, or on the other hand merely *senescent* or in the "last stages" of extinction may be a matter for argument. Again it may be important to make a distinction between

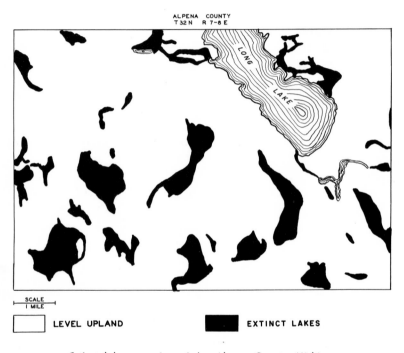

ALPENA COUNTY
T 32 N   R 7-8 E

SCALE
1 MILE

LEVEL UPLAND   EXTINCT LAKES

Extinct lakes near Long Lake, Alpena County, Michigan.

an "extinct lake" and a feature which is merely a dry basin which at one time contained a lake. *Extinction* as a concept differs from *destruction* such as that caused by some catastrophic happening in nature, or the obliteration of lakes brought about by man.

See: *paleo lake*

extralegal access

Extralegal access is involved when a person gains access to a lake over land not owned by himself, over private property without permission or over public property that is riparian in location but is devoid of riparian rights, such as the right of way of a public road.

Extralegal implies that the right of the person to use the water is unsettled or moot.

extralegal riparian

A person who becomes a riparian by virtue of the extension inland of the water of a lake beyond its natural

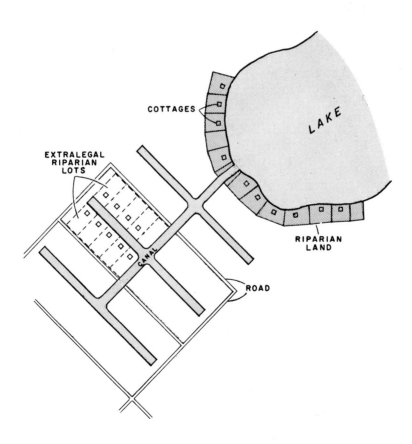

Dredged canal to provide access for new lake subdivision.

banks or shoreline. By excavation, inlets may be widened or deepened and extended inland, and connecting channels with bays, lagoons and boatways made which provide water frontage for land owners who would otherwise be non-riparians.

fall overturn

A phenomenon that may take place in a lake in early autumn. Beginning with a cooling of the surface waters and a change in density, a general circulation or mixing of the water from top to bottom takes place, resulting in physical and chemical uniformity, which may be referred to as the initial phase of winter stagnation.

false beach

A bar, above water level, a short distance off shore.

false bottom (lake)

A colloquial term usually applied to a semi-suspended or soupy organic mass through which a weight easily sinks. Soft marl is also referred to very frequently as a false bottom.

false ponds

Mirage effects in desert regions, which resemble water bodies.

false shoreline

The line of contact between the open water of a lake and the front, or edge, or a "floating" mat of vegetation built out from the shore. Here the mat does not represent a former, and higher stage of the lake and is therefore technically a part of the lake, even though its surface may be above water level.

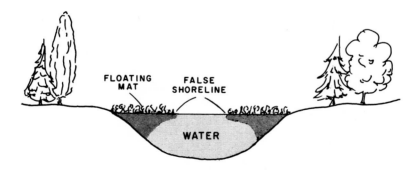

In some lakes the marginal water is very shallow and the emergent vegetation is so dense that the shoreline is indefinite. Often the zone of vegetation terminates abruptly lakeward making a secondary or "false shoreline".

far shore

In reference to a single access route terminating at the shore, the far shore would be located on the opposite side of the lake.

Photo – Soil Conservation Service, East Lansing, Michigan

Farm Ponds

farm pond

A small shallow structure constructed for the impound-ment of water; agricultural water needs include irrigation, stock watering, spray water and fire protection. Usually the pond site is a natural depression which is deepened to store surface runoff.

Most of the farm ponds in Michigan are excavated deep enough to utilize ground water but some are designed to capture surface run off. A few ponds are created by building dams on small streams.

In some instances the pond structure merely provides temporary storage for water pumped from a lake, stream or well, but most farmers have permanent ponds that also provide recreational benefits; fishing, boating, bathing, wildfowl habitat, picnicking, and aesthetic values.

The current need for surface water is strongly reflected by the vast number of farm ponds being constructed throughout the United States.

See: *pond*

fast ice

Ice attached to and extending out from the land. In contrast to *floe* ice, or *drift* ice.

feather rights

A colloquialism for the wildfowl hunting rights attached to inland lakes and streams.

fecal matter

Animal excrement. The presence of fecal matter of human origin in water would indicate that untreated sewage had been discharged. Qualitatively, this is the most obnoxious form of *pollution* or *smirchment* on inland lakes.

Federal Waters, inland

The designation Federal applies to inland waters, including lakes, that are used for commercial navigation. Boating on Federal Waters is subject to the navigation rules of the U. S. Coast Guard. Some of the inland lakes, connected with or tributary to the Great Lakes, that are navigable by federal test may be subject to Coast Guard rules and control.

feindetritus gyttja

Lake bottom deposits derived mainly from plankton. (Naumann)

fen

A British term sometimes used in the United States and often loosely as the equivalent of marsh, bog and swamp. Technically the term *fen* may be restricted to a marsh or bog that has an alkaline mucky or non-peaty soil. The landward, or peripheral zone of an acid bog surrounding a lake, may be called "marginal fen" because the soil is more humified.

fertile lake

Lakes are often described as being *fertile* or *infertile*. A "fertile lake" is one that has a large standing crop, that is, a prolific growth of aquatic plants and usually accompanying prolific aquatic fauna. The degree of fertility *cannot* be measured or determined solely by chemical analysis of the waters or bottom soil.

Chemical tests of the water may reveal extreme acidity, alkalinity, salinity or presence of toxic matter and afford an explanation why a lake is unproductive, or has only a meager biomass.

See: *eutrophication*

fertilized lake

One to which plant nutrients have been added in the form of commercial fertilizer, manure, or any other amendments for the purpose of increasing lake productivity.

Influents or affluents may carry nutrients in solution or suspension into a lake; an increase in plant production results from pollution such as that from sewage and the effluent from sewage treatment.

fetch

On a lake surface, the reach, or the longest distance over which the wind can sweep unobstructed.

field investigation (lake)

A field investigation involves on site examination of a lake as opposed to an office study and review of records.

fill (lake)

The artificial deposition of sand, gravel, spoil from dredging, or other material on the submerged land or low shore land of a lake. The usual purposes: improvement of the shore land for cottage sites and other structures, extension of riparian ownership, dams to raise lake levels, roads and causeways, improvement of beaches. Natural fills may take place by the deposition of organic and inorganic sediments, resulting in beaches, bars, islands, shoals, and mud flats.

See: *accretion*
alluvion
delta lakes
purgatorial reliction

filled frontage

Artificial land, made by filling, which fronts on the waters of a lake; in contrast to natural shoreline land, or the natural land level. The usual purpose of the filled

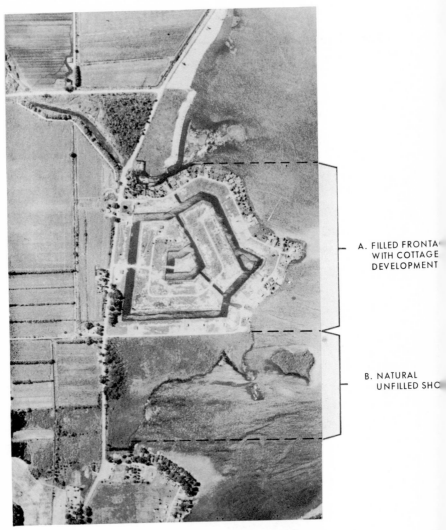

A. FILLED FRONTA
WITH COTTAGE
DEVELOPMENT

B. NATURAL
UNFILLED SHC

South End of Gun Lake, Barry County, Michigan.

frontage is to provide access to open or deep water and so by this and other resulting improvements increase use potential and property values.

See: *fill*
    frontage

filter dams

Pervious dams of loose stones, or stones and brush, placed in outlets of lakes to prevent fish from moving out; or at the mouths of inlet streams to prevent fish from entering.

finger lakes

Long, narrow lakes occupying deep troughs in deeply eroded straight pre-glacial valleys in glaciated regions.

"Finger" is frequently used as a descriptive term and in place name for lakes, regardless of origin, on the basis of a close, or only a faint, resemblance in shape to a finger of the human hand.

firm shore

See: *hard shore*

fish kill

Destruction of fish in lakes or ponds due to prolonged ice and snow cover and resulting oxygen deficiency; or in very shallow lakes due to freezing of the water down to the bottom; or in summer due to oxygen deficiency caused by excessive amounts of organic matter in suspension. Also, fish may be killed by toxic pollutants or disease.

See: *freeze-out lakes*
    icthyotoxin
    winterkill

fish ladder

Any device designed to facilitate the movement of migrating fish over a dam. A conventional fish ladder consists of a stair-like series of small ponds connected by flowing water. The fish may swim from pond to pond and gain access to the lake or reservoir. Varying degrees of success are claimed by those involved with the administration of fish ladders.

fish poison

See: *icthyotoxin*

fish sanctuary

A place where fishing has been permanently forbidden by statute.

fishery

The term fishery of an inland lake is used in a special sense pertaining to the total game fish population and its environment. On the Great Lakes and larger inland lakes the term is ordinarily used to include the economic aspects of commercial fishing.

fission lakes

Lakes which represent division of, or separation from, an original single body of water. In Michigan numerous instances can be cited where natural drainage and uneven filling in a compound basin, the latter usually followed by recession in lake level, leaves a number of separate lakes in the "holes", or deeper parts of the original basin. Also where a lake had a very irregular shoreline the bays or deep indentations may be cut off or detached from the main body by the formation of bars at their mouths, thus forming separate lakes. Separate lakes may be formed in deltas, or a lake may be divided by a fluviatile dam caused by sediments carried in by flowing streams, and sometimes a portion of a lake has been cut off from the main body by a beaver dam. In other locations there are lakes associated with beaches and dunes where the shifting of sands by storm waves and by wind action has produced a division in the water body. In Michigan, the number of

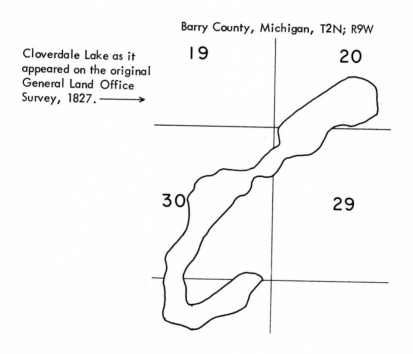

Barry County, Michigan, T2N; R9W

Cloverdale Lake as it appeared on the original General Land Office Survey, 1827. ⟶

19

20

30

29

lakes which have become extinct since early post-glacial time has been offset in some measure by the number of *fission* lakes.

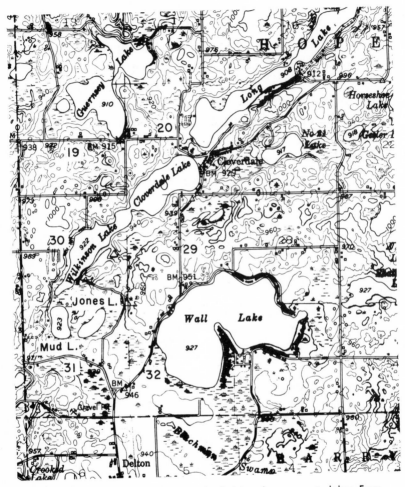

The single lake of 1827 has been divided into four separate lakes. From U.S.G.S. Hastings Quadrangle (T2N; R9W), 1951.

flagstone ice
Large, floating, flat fragments resulting from the break up of sheets of tabular ice.

flagstone pavement
See: *boulder pavement*

121

flats

In relation to lakes, and other bodies of standing water: the low lying exposed parts of lake deltas; the flat lands of alluvial plains subject to flooding; and the recently exposed flat bottoms of lakes are often so called. Examples in Michigan are: The St. Clair Flats, the marsh land of the delta of Lake St. Clair; and the Shiawassee Flats, the flat lands at the junctions of the Shiawassee, Flint and Cass Rivers which were originally covered with water for extended periods, (and at one time known as Shiawassee Lake) and are now flooded as a wild life and recreational preserve.

In the arid parts of western U. S., the flat bottoms of desiccated lakes are called flats.

fleet boats

Boats owned by the operator of a livery or marina for rental to the public. All are registered under the operator's name and are usually used at one location for an entire season.

Rental businesses are operated at many locations to meet the increased demand for water craft by the recreational public. Many families prefer to rent equipment rather than accept the high initial investment, storage and maintenance costs. Demand is no longer limited to hand propelled row boats; large and luxurious cabin cruisers may be rented or chartered for variable time periods.

See: *moored boat*
transient boat

floatage

Use of surface water for floating material from one location to another location for a beneficial purpose. Many lakes and streams in United States and Canada have been used for floating logs to mills.

floating aquatic plant

A free floating plant such as the duckweeds; or one partly floating that is rooted to the bottom but has floating leaves such as the water shield *(Brasenia)* and white water lily *(Nymphaea)*.

floating island

A free floating mat of vegetation. These floating mats usually represent a mass detached from a shore of quaking bog or marsh by storms or by a rise in lake level.

floating sand

A patch of floating sand is a phenomenon occasionally observed on the calm water of a lake. The dry sand particles float because they are unable to break the surface tension of the water.

floats

Small bouyant objects made from plastic or other material, anchored off beaches to indicate the danger area for bathers. Also used to mark lanes for racing boats.

See: *buoy*

flood zone

Some large reservoirs, impoundments of streams, are subject to a wide rise in level during a season of high precipitation. The area of shore land inundated by the rise in level above the normal operating pool level is the *flood zone*.

See: *floodplain*

flooding

A term which applies to water bodies, which inundate, or cover flat lands as a thin sheet. The water may be

Photo — Wisconsin Department of Conservation

Meadow Valley wildlife flooding, Wisconsin. Note dam in foreground.

backed up by dams, or created by diversion of natural drainage ways on to flats where containment is effected by building dikes or levees. Floodings may be created to serve primarily as feeding and nesting grounds for water fowl or for shooting preserves, but may also serve other purposes, such as fishing waters. The hydronym FLOOD-ING, further identified by a specific geographic name, is frequently applied, especially where the water is a part of a wildlife project.

floodplain (of a lake)

That part of a lake basin plain, lying between the shoreline and the shore cliff and subject to submergence during a high stage of the lake.

floodwater

An impoundment; a word sometimes applied as a proper name to the flooded area back of a dam, similar to *Reservoir, Lake, Pond* and *Flowage.*

floodwoods

A term used by American pioneers for natural ob-structions of driftwood, transported by flood waters of rivers. In some Michigan rivers the wood, tree trunks and pieces of all sizes, in instances accumulated in tight jams as much as 500 or 600 feet long which were known as *rafts.* The *floodwoods* made portages necessary in canoe travel; produced areas of backwater, diverted and spread stream channels.

Similar rafts of driftwood on the Yukon River, Alaska have been called "woodyards". (I. C. Russell, Lakes of North America, page 27)

floor (of a lake)

The lower or deeper lying part of the bottom, especially of a deep lake. The term *floor* is often used interchangeably with *bed* and *bottom.* However, for many particular kinds of standing water bodies it seems appropriate to make a distinction. In some instances of usage flatness or horizontality is implied; and it is also limited to the firm surface lying beneath soft autogenic deposits, but commonly these interpretations are not observed.

See: *bottom*

flot

See: *pond scum*

flotant (floating marsh)

"A type of coastal marsh formed along most of the abandoned channels and in many of the low basins between the natural levees of both inactive and active stream channels" (Russell, R. J., *Geographical Review*, Vol. XXXII, No. 1, January 1962, pp. 74-98) in southern Louisiana, south of New Orleans. It is intermediate between open water on the one hand and firm marshland on the other.

flotsam

Ship wreckage or cargo tossed overboard and found floating. Also, with reference to lakes, the word is used with the meaning, any kind of floating debris.

flow line

The edge of the water of a reservoir indicating the maximum level stipulated in the rights to flood land. Also called *flowage line*.

flowage

The volume or dimensions of the water of a stream. As a legal term flowage may refer to rainfall or any other waters which run off higher land, (but not concentrated in a single stream) and flow over adjacent lower land. "Flowage" is also in use as a part of the place name for the area of water impounded by a dam for power, and thus is used interchangeably with reservoir, basin, pond, and floodwater. "Flowage land" is that which will be covered by the water impounded by a proposed dam. The word *flowage* is also an attributive as in the legal term "flowage rights."

> See: *flowage easement*
> *flowage rights*

flowage easement

The right to flow a tract of land to a designated level; usually sold voluntarily. The land owner may reserve the right to enter upon and use the entire flowage for riparian purposes but he always retains ownership to the bottom-land located on his tract. Ingress and egress may be across an exclusive or semi-exclusive right of way between the uppermost contour elevation established by the easement and the waterline. The right to flow land usually embodies the right to manipulate the water level.

flowage land

Flowage land is that which will be covered by the water impounded by a proposed dam, exclusive of the river bed.

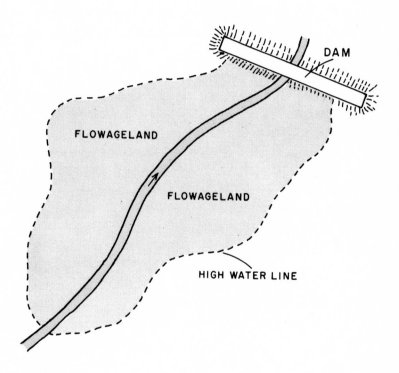

flowage rights

The legal rights of the vendee to flow and use the water of a reservoir or flooding. His rights may be general (to make any use whatsoever) or limited (for power purposes). It is usually assumed that the water level will be manipulated but controversy may be avoided by clearly defining the rights transferred to the vendee. The vendor may also desire to list his rights covering access and to use the reservoir or flooding; such as for fishing, trapping, hunting and boating.

flushing period

The time required for an amount of water equal to the volume of the lake to pass through its outlet.

fluvial lakes

In usage the term *lake* is not always restricted to standing water bodies, but on the contrary is sometimes applied to waters which have a perceptible flow. Examples of fluvial lakes are: ventricose distentions or simple expansions in the width of a river; widewaters; connecting channels in the nature of sloughs; an impoundment back of a dam or other obstruction across a stream; a wide channel of water, without laterals or tributaries; connected water bodies with small differences in elevation, but sufficient to create a flow from one to the other, such as the connecting water bodies between Lakes Superior and Huron. In practice the distinction between a *river* and a *lake* is not always sharp, or consistent.

fluviatile lake

A lake formed in the flood plain of a river such as an ox-bow lake, or other water body formed as a result of stream erosion and deposition.

foam

Lake water having a relatively high quantity of organic acids in solution has a tendency to foam. Synthetic detergents will also cause foaming.

See: *suds*

foam line

The forward line of a broken wave advancing into shallow water as a positive surge or wave of translation.

See: *wind streaks*

forebay

A small pond, or reservoir, at the head of the penstock of a hydroelectric power plant.

foreland (lake shores)

A *head* or *headland;* the use of the term in this sense is infrequent.

See: *cuspate foreland*

foreshore

See: *beach profile* for illustration

The part of a shore, or beach, normally subject to the uprush and backrush of waves.

See: *backshore*

forna-gyttja

Lake bottom deposit composed largely of the remains of higher aquatic plants; coarser texture than *ävja.*

See: *gyttja*

fosse lakes

Glacial lakes occupying a depression lying between the front of a moraine and its outwash plain.

fossil lake

One that has been extinct for a long period of time; or a *paleo* lake, one that existed in a past geologic period.

fowling grounds

That part of a lake's surface or associated marsh frequented by waterfowl, feeding or resting during the hunting season.

freeze-out lake

A localism for a very shallow lake subject to being frozen over deeply and for prolonged periods. A result of the freezing is complete, or nearly complete destruction of fish.

See: *fish kill*

freshettes (lake)

Small affluent streams which have a high rate of flow during the spring season and often carry a heavy silt load during their peak flow.

frog pond

One that has a habitat favorable for the production of edible frogs. Also, the term may have derisive or derogatory implications where applied to a body of water.

front lots (of a lake)

See: *back lots* for illustration

Platted lots fronting directly on a lake. Front lots would normally be riparian lots unless certain or all riparian rights were reserved by the vendor.

frontage (lake)

Land bordering the shoreline, fronting the lake and extending to the water line. However, in some commercial lake development promotional plans, the term is used loosely and not all individual parcels of "frontage" land actually extend to the water line.

fulls

In England the term has been applied to beach ridges. Where there is a succession of ridges on a shore, each representing an advance in a shoreline, the ridge is called a "full" and the depression between a "swale".

funnel access

A small parcel of riparian land deeded collectively to a large group of back lot owners which enables them to gain legal access to the lake surface.

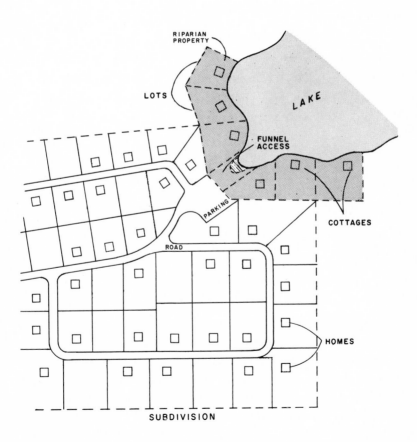

funnel development (lake)

A real estate development procedure by which a large number of non-riparian lot owners become part owners of a small riparian access tract and therefore gain legal access to a lake, through the "funnel" of riparian land.

fusion lakes

Two or more lakes which are separate in nature may be joined, or "fused" into a single water body. Artificial fusion, the joining of two or more lakes by flooding or by excavation of the land separating them is not uncommon. *Fusion* may also take place by natural processes; (1) Oxbow lakes and sloughs of river flood plains may be joined by river flood waters; (2) separate water bodies may be combined by backwater from natural dams, as rafts, floodwoods and beaver dams; (3) from flooding in swamps, marshes or glades following periods of heavy precipitation; (4) fusion may be due to local rises in the level of the ground water table. Some of the above *fusion lakes* may be merely ephemeral but others may be permanent and of significant economic value. However, the total number of these lakes in Michigan is insignificant in comparison with the number created by fission.

See: *fission lakes*

gabion

A specially designed basket or box of corrosion resistant wire used to hold rock and other coarse aggregate. These gabions may be locked together to form groins, sea walls, revetments, deflectors and other structures. Their flexible construction permits minor adjustments of alignment resulting from undercutting, filling and settling.

gang of lakes

A cluster of lakes, 4 or 5 to 10 or 12, not arranged in any definite pattern, and connected, or not, but included in a relatively small land area. A "gang" may consist of remnants, of what was originally a single large body of water, set in a marsh or swamp terrain.

See: *chain of lakes*
  swarm of lakes

gap

A passage or narrow channel between shoreland and an island. In Lake of the Woods, Canada gap is used as a generic; Devils Gap.

gator holes

A localism (Florida) for small pools in swamps, especially solution holes in limestone in the Everglades.

glacial lakes

The term *glacial* applies to those lakes formed as a result of glacial action during the Pleistocene. The sites of extinct glacial lakes may be determined by old beach and shoreline features and lacustrine sediments. The term *glacial* is also applied to lakes associated with existing, or present-day, glaciers.

glade

Among its several connotations, *glade* may mean a water covered marsh or wet prairie. However, geographic instances of *glades* of this kind, other than the Everglades of Florida, are very infrequent.

Glade has been used as a term for a stretch of open water in the ice of a lake or river but instances of usage in this sense are not common.

glint lakes

A term of Norwegian origin applied to Glacial lakes resulting from ice-filled pre-glacial valleys where the ice mass moved from the filled valley into mountain passes eventually leaving lakes in the passes or divides. The term has been applied to certain lakes in Norway and Scotland. A brief mention of the occurrence of swamps and lakes on glaciated cols and stream divides, with an example in Pennsylvania, was made by N. S. Shaler. (Tenth Annual Report, U. S. Geological Survey, Part 1, 1888-89, page 301)

goose pool

An artificial pool that is stocked with captive wild geese for public observation.

government lot

In the General Land Office survey of the public domain, tracts of land within a section, consisting of fractional

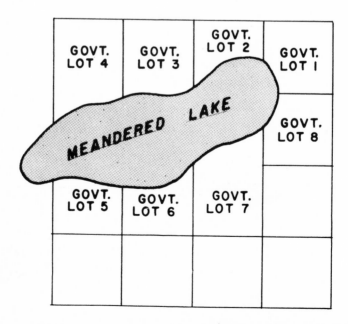

quarters and 40's, were designated "lots". Fractional lots were common on the borders of meandered lakes, because section lines and land lines were extended, with few exceptions, only to the shoreline of the lake.

graben lake
>   See: *rift lakes*

gradient (of lake bottom)
>   The inclination, from the horizontal, of the lake bottom beginning at the shore line. Usually means the same as *slope*.
>   The gradient of the bottom, especially near the shore-line, whether gentle or steep, is an important factor in the evaluation of a lake.

grass beach
>   Artificial grass beaches have been constructed on reservoirs in Ohio. Piling is driven into the water at a shallow

GRASS BEACH

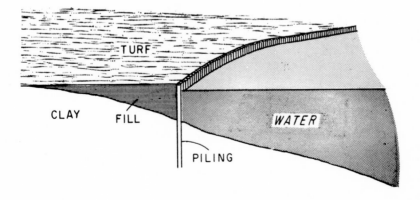

depth and back filled to the upland. After the fill is surfaced with soil, turf can be maintained as a grass beach. The grass beach is more servicable for recreational use than the original clay and silt shore.

grass lakes

Grass as an element in a place name for a lake is common but it is also a demotic applied to very shallow, marshy lakes supporting a grassy vegetation consisting of true grasses and "false grasses", the latter mostly sedges. "Grass lake" is sometimes applied to a marsh, not water covered, occupying the bed of a former lake.

gravel pit lakes

In the mining of gravel, from the glacial drift, in Michigan and other states, excavations often extend far below the level of the water table, and when mining operations are abandoned, bodies of open water, often of considerable size, are left. Usually the gravel pit lake is bordered by steep bare slopes which descend into deep water at the shoreline, and the environment is unsightly debris from mining operations. However, in favorable locations, gravel pit lakes have been successfully modified and developed for recreational uses. Bordering land may also be improved as a residential subdivision. Abandoned ponds are often used as swimming holes by youngsters but constitute a serious hazard because of deep cold water.

Great Ponds

In 1641, the Massachussets Bay Colony decreed that "Great Ponds" meaning those bodies of fresh water, 10 acres or more in size, should forever remain open to the public for fishing and fowling.

Photo – Michigan Department of Conservation

An operating gravel pit.

"green" sands

Sands having a greenish color, due to attached algae, observed on lake beaches and shoals.

grobdetritus gyttja

Lake bottom deposits coarse and fibrous in texture.

groin (groyne)

A low narrow wall-like structure extending out into the lake normal to the shore. It may be constructed of

Groins on shore of Lake Michigan.

timber, stone, concrete or steel and is usually impermeable. Its purpose is to catch littoral drift, or to trap sand, and to protect a beach from destructive erosion. Sometimes called a *wing dam.*

ground water lake

One whose water represents the level of the ground water or the upper boundary of the zone of saturation.

A ground water lake is said to represent an exposure of the water table. In contrast some lakes receive their water directly from precipitation and from surface run-off.

In a number of locations the water surfaces of lakes closely associated vary considerably in elevation. In such instances a lake surface may not represent *the* ground water table, but rather *a* ground water table.

See: *perched lake*

ground water recharge pond

A shallow pond made by excavation in relatively coarse, permeable material near a water well field. Water from a nearby stream may be diverted into the recharge pond, thereby providing a continuous supply of water that infiltrates through the pond bottom and percolates downward to the aquifer. The capacity of the wells, within the influence of the recharge pond, are greatly enhanced. If sediment is carried into the recharge pond, the sediment can be cleaned out or the pond bottom can be loosened up to facilitate infiltration.

group camp lake

A lake dedicated and developed for group camping: Boy Scouts, 4-H, YWCA, YMCA, church and fraternal groups.

gum ponds

A localism in Southern States for shallow ponds bordered by gum trees, (species of *Nyssa*), or having these trees standing in the water.

gyttja

A term employed by limnologists and pedologists for the deposition on the bottoms of lakes, which is organic

or inorganic or various mixtures of the two.
A Swedish folkname, pronounced yüttya.

See: *ävja gyttja*
feindetritus
forna qyttja
grobdetritus
kalkgyttja
ochregyttja

habitat (lake)
The total of the environmental conditions which affect the life of plants and animals. Each lake or part of a lake has its own peculiar habitat.

hairy lake
In the Canoe Country of Canada, deep marshes are sometimes called *hairy lakes* because standing sedge, reed and rush vegetation observed from a distance bears some similarity to hair.

hanging cottage
One built on the face of a lake shore cliff or a steep declivity, bordering a lake. A building technique utilizing piling makes it possible to construct this type of cottage.

harbor line
On the Great Lakes, a line (set by Army Corps of Engineers) beyond which no wharfs can be constructed.

harbor of refuge
A name given to havens on the shores of the Great Lakes located in between commercial harbors, and designed primarily to be a place of refuge for small craft during storm periods.

harbors

A place of safe anchorage for ships and pleasure craft. Harbors are geographic features on the shore lines of the Great Lakes, but havens on the inland lakes are rarely called *harbors*.

hard

A firm natural shore suitable as a landing place. Mainly British and not in common usage in the United States but in the sense given, it has a useful place in the vocabulary of *Lacology*.

hard shore

Shoreline material composed of sand, gravel, cobbles, boulders, or bed rock.

See: *softshore*

hardwater lake

One whose waters contain a high concentration of mineral salts, especially bicarbonates of calcium and magnesium, in solution. In Michigan, the lakes commonly regarded as *hardwater* contain more than 100 parts per million of calcium and magnesium. Other metallic ions, such as iron, produce hardness, but very probably are not in significant amounts except in a relatively few lakes.

hatch, insect

Under favorable environmental conditions, mayflies and other aquatic insects hatch or change to adults in vast numbers during a relatively short period of time. Pupae cases and adults may literally cover the lake surface and myriads of flying adults may interfere with some lake uses.

head (of bay)

The part of the shoreline of the bay extending farthest inland.

head (of lake)

The influent (stream) end, or where no single influent is present the end opposite the outlet. The term has no application to lakes in enclosed basins. Where an influent enters a lake very near the outlet the term is inapplicable, and also in numerous other instances where a number of small affluents enter a lake; or where a lake is nearly a perfect circle in shape.

head of outlet

The place where the water leaves the lakes and enters the outlet stream, or effluent.

headland (lake)

A highland projection of a shoreline. Also the steep front of a promontory. However, often in usage there appears to be no sharp distinction between *head; headland; point; and cape.* Two *headlands* may enclose, or form the sides of a bay and sometimes the ends are connected by a bar.

headrace

A race constructed to lead water to a water wheel or into an industrial building.

headwaters lake

One located in the upper reaches of a river with small or no inlet streams. A lake of this kind is less subject to water pollution than one located farther down stream.

headwaters mark
A mark which limits the height, or level of water permitted back of a dam.

herbicide
Any substance which kills herbaceous plants. Aquatic plants frequently become a nuisance in lakes and herbicides may be used for their eradication or control.

highwater mark
The position which the water line of a lake holds for the greatest part of a period of time. Where a lake is subject to considerable wave action the high water mark is clearly and definitely indicated by a nip or wave-cut bank; elsewhere the natural soil and vegetation above the ordinary water line will have a character distinctively different from that below it. The term "high water mark" has legal connotations and is used in court decisions involving private and riparian ownership and rights on lakes where no water level data are available, as opposed to state control and ownership of lake water and lake bottoms. The term is used synonymously with *ordinary high water mark.* The following entries have pertinence to this term: *eoshore; neoshore; reliction; purgatorial reliction; stage (of a lake).*

holding pond (hatchery)
A pond or pool at a fish hatchery which is used for holding fish which have been reared for planting or to commercial size and are awaiting shipment.

holding pond (industrial)
The term is applied to ponds which hold waste from factories prior to its final discharge into a stream, or other final disposal. Also called *holding lagoon.*

hole

In usage in the U. S. the term has been applied to several widely different kinds of depressional features, both very small and very large, both wet and dry. In numerous locations, it is a local name for a small lake, or pond, occupying a sink, closed pit or hollow which may be either deep or shallow. *Hole* is also a name for a deep hollow and deep water, in a lake basin, and for either shallow or deep pockets containing water set in the terrain of a marsh or swamp. "Holes" are often identified by a geographic name, and occasionally in such names the generic Hole Lake is used. Also locally a bay of a lake, especially if the bay is "landlocked", is sometimes called a "hole."

See: *pothole*
sink lakes
waterhole

holm lake

One dotted with islands.

holomictic lake

One in which the circulation, or mixing, of the waters takes place throughout the entire depth. In contrast to a *meromictic lake* in which circulation is only in the upper layers and not complete.

hook

A spit of sand or gravel turned landward at the outer end.

horizontal rainbow

A relatively rare phenomenon on some lakes resulting from the reflection and refraction of light from mist above the lake surface.

hot pond
In lumbering in the Lake States, small storage ponds, containing logs to be sawed, heated with steam to prevent freezing, and interference with sawing operations, in winter, were called hot ponds.

houseboat
The houseboat, for seasonal or year round dwelling is permitted on lakes in some states. Usually such structures, either on boats or on floats are anchored near the shoreline, and are subject to regulations for the disposal of sewage and garbage to prevent pollution.

Houseboats on Basswood Lake, Boundary Waters Canoe Area, Minnesota.

humus lake
A dystrophic lake; one that contains a large amount of humic matter in solution or suspension in its waters.

hydraulic dredge, lake

A machine, usually mounted upon a barge, which has a submersible cutting head to loosen up bottom material. The loosened material is sucked up by a pump, along with water, and forced through a floating pipeline to a disposal area. Usually, provision is made for the water to drain back into the lake from the disposal area.

hydrograph (lake)

A graph showing the stages, or variations in lake level, over a period of time.

hydrographic basin (lake)

The area of the watershed of a lake plus the area (size), of the lake.

Hydrophyte

See: *aquatic plants, lake*

Hydrosols, water soils

A major pedologic group distinquished from: (1) mineral soils and (2) organic soils (peats and mucks). Lakes as soils are *Hydrosols*.

See: *aquasol*

hypolimnion

In a thermally stratified lake, the layer of water below the *thermocline* and extending to the bottom of the lake; water temperature is virtually uniform.

ice action line

The on-shore high mark reached by the ice of a solidly frozen over lake.

ice barrier basins

Glaciers descending mountain valleys may obstruct the

lower ends of tributary valleys thus damming the tributary streams and forming lakes. Basins of this origin have been called *ice barrier basins.*

ice boats

Sleds or boats on runners provided with sails or motors for movement and designed for pleasure and sporting events on the ice of smoothly frozen over lakes.

ice damage

Damage to cultural improvements and to natural features along the lake shore caused by ice expansion or by *ice rafts* and *jams.*

ice jams

Masses of broken-up lake ice, drifted and piled up by wind. The ice may be piled up, on or against a lake shore with tremendous pressure and produce various modifications of shore deposits and damage lakeshore improvements.

ice lake

One from which ice is harvested in winter, and stored under insulation for summer, or any later use. Cutting and storage of ice from lakes once important is now a vanishing industry. The right to harvest ice from an inland lake in Michigan is the exclusive right of the riparian.

ice push

The movement on the shore of the solid ice sheet, of a frozen-over lake, due to expansion. The *push* or *shove* action on yielding shore material may produce a rampart

Transient ice push, soft bottom material, west side of Houghton Lake, Michigan.

or ridge. Under some circumstances ice may push soft bottom material onto the shore in the form of ridges, but usually such ridges are transient.

See: *walled lakes*

ice push terrace

A shore feature formed where the expansion of the ice of frozen over lakes pushes up successive ridges of gravel or other detritus to substantially the same heights.

ice raft
An extensive sheet of ice, detached and floating freely in open water.

ice rampart
A ridge of debris or wall, on a lake shore, formed by ice push.

Ice rampart, Indian Lake. From Scott, I. D., *Inland Lakes of Michigan*, Michigan Geological Survey, Publication No. 30, 1921.

ice road
A temporary winter road constructed across the frozen surface of a lake or stream. Ice roads are used most frequently for trucking forest or mineral products but on occasion service sportsmen. In instances, for example Lake Baikal, Russia, temporary railroad tracks are also laid on frozen lakes.

ice rights

Well-defined rights possessed by riparians to harvest or use ice offshore from their land.

ice shanty

A very small portable house or other enclosure used by fishermen on frozen over lakes as a protection from

Photo — Michigan Tourist Council
Ice shanties on Houghton Lake, Michigan.

severe weather. The "shanty" is set over a hole, cut or bored, through which fishing is done.

ice shove
>See: *ice push*

ice spud
>An implement used by fishermen to cut a hole in the ice of a frozen-over lake.

icthyotoxin
>Any substance which kills fish. Frequently used to eliminate or control rough fish populations and to manage

Photo – Wisconsin Conservation Department

Spraying fish poison (icthyotoxin) on a lake.

lakes with overstocked or stunted populations of pan fish.

Rotenone, a natural derivative of the South American derris root has been widely used throughout the world as an *icthyotoxin* but today there are many synthetic materials used with variable success.

Proper use of *icthyotoxins* requires technical knowledge of the lake involved and most frequently a permit is required from the conservation agency having jurisdiction over fishing.

Future availability of highly selective *icthyotoxins* will perhaps facilitate the management of inland waters.

impounding reservoir

One in which water is held for a considerable period of time and released to increase or maintain stream flow.

impoundment

A body of water ponded, or held back by a dam, dike, floodgate or any other barrier. The word *impoundment* is generally a common noun, and only rarely has an attached specific to make it a place name. No sharp technical distinction exists between an *impoundment* and a *flooding*.

improvements (lake)

Modifications of natural conditions or changes in the environment in a lake or on its shoreland presumably for the betterment for some particular use, or for the purpose of increasing property values. However, because of the diversity of interests in lake use, and opposing philosophies of land use, the same modification may be regarded either as a betterment or on the other hand a detriment and impairment. In some special instances for example, *wilderness lakes*, any "improvements" whatsoever may be opposed.

Examples of improvements:
Filling along the shoreline or to create islands
Dredging
Building beaches
Aquatic weed planting or removal
Planting or removal of fish
Lake level stabilization
Fertilization
Building underwater structures for fish habitat
Increase of size
Wildfowl habitat improvement
Predator control

indicator organism

See: *pollution indicator organism*

infiltration lagoon

See: *ground water recharge pond*

influent (of lake)

See: *inlet* for illustration

Any surface stream flowing into a lake in contrast to an outflowing stream, or *effluent.* Often used synonymously with *inlet* and *affluent.* In a hydrologic sense, ground water may be influent in the form of springs or seepage.

See: *inlet*

ingress (onto a lake)

Ingress is legally restricted to the act of entering onto a lake. As a solitary right *ingress* would have little value unless coupled with *egress* or the right of departure from a *lake.*

See: *egress*

inland lakes

Those lying inland from sea coasts; by analogy "inland" is employed with reference to the Great Lakes. "Inland lakes" serve especially in Michigan and Wisconsin, as a group term to distinguish the interior bodies, that is, those lying back from the shores, and from the waters of the Great Lakes.

Some connected water bodies, though lying inland from the shores may be a part of the navigable water of the Great Lakes, and therefore wholly or in part, under the jurisdiction of the Corps of Army Engineers and Coast Guard of the U. S. Government.

inland waterway

See: *waterway*

inlet

A surface stream which enters a lake; or the place of entrance of inflowing water. When an inland lake is

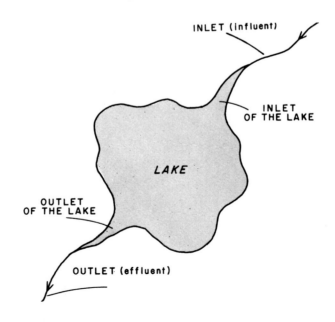

described as having an inlet, most commonly a single in-flowing surface stream of considerable size is implied. In some instances of usage an estuary, a narrow cove, arm, tongue or reach of the lake extending into the land may be called an *inlet*. Also, a cut, pass or connecting channel which permits inflow may be an inlet.

When, in descriptions a lake is said to have an *inlet*, meaning an inflowing stream, this information alone has little hydrologic or economic significance; facts about the inflowing stream, its volume, permanency of flow, navigability, etc. are needed.

The word influent is restricted in meaning to an inflowing stream; the word *inlet* may be used in the same sense, but also has other connotations.

See: *influent*

in-line flowages

Two or more closely spaced flowages on a stream or river. Such a series of in-line flowages especially if shallow are more likely to create problems of low dissolved oxygen concentration and increased temperature.

inner beach

That part of a sandy beach which is covered by the wash of gentle waves, and ordinarily is saturated.

inshore

The reference is to water area bordering and lying very near the shoreline.

See: *offshore*

inside pond

See: *outside pond*

insulosity

The percentage of the area of a lake that is occupied by islands.

Lake characterized by a high percentage area of islands. Lake Insula, Minnesota.

intake whirlpool

Some hydro-electric power stations have under water intakes located on the bottom of the reservoir. During periods of low water level the inflowing water creates a clockwise circulation pattern that depresses the water surface directly over the intake and creates a small whirlpool.

intermittent island

A patch of shallow bottom that is exposed during a period of low lake level and is covered again when the lake returns to its normal level.

intermittent lake

One that normally contains water for the greater part of the year and is only seasonally dry. Some lakes may have widely fluctuating water levels but never become completely dry; others, extinct or near extinct, may be partly filled with water during wet seasons or after rains. A peculiar kind of intermittency occurs in some lime sink lakes having subterranean outlets. The basins of such lakes may remain dry for an extended indefinite period, and later the basin may become filled and remain a live lake for an indefinite period.

See: *ephemeral lakes*

iridesence

Rainbow colors may appear on lake water, because of refraction of light, where an oil film or a film of ferric hydroxide exists on the surface of the water.

irregular basin

A lake basin whose floor is characterized by variations in depth, shallows and deeps; or by marked inequalities in relief such as a submerged knob and kettle type of topography.

irregular shoreline

One marked by indentations, inlets, bays, and headlands, promontories, or points, in contrast to a smooth unbroken curved or straight line.

Irregular shoreline, Lake Saganaga, Boundary Waters Canoe Area, Minnesota.

island (lake)

An area of land, within a lake, completely surrounded by water. In usage, this definition is not strictly observed. *Island* may be applied to land-tied areas; to submerged bodies, or *blind islands*, and *sunken islands*; and to upland in marsh or bog backland of lakes.

The word *island* is applied to extremely small, as well as to relatively large bodies of land, both in place names and geographic descriptions.

The number, size, and distribution of islands have significance in relation to the biologic productivity, the recreational values and navigational use of a lake.

Rock island.

On large lakes the term island is applied to any rock or soil feature large enough to stand on. Many are merely rounded rock outcrops, polished by over riding ice and frequently submerged by impoundments. Such submergence frequently results in conflicts of interest, because islands have a high value for cottage sites and camping.

See: *blind island*
insulosity
presque isle
quondam island
sidd
sunken island
tombolo

(See next page for Lake Islands Classification)

LAKE ISLANDS CLASSIFICATION

I. CONSEQUENT (ORIGINAL) ISLANDS

A. Glacial drift islands
1. Bordered by submerged shelf
2. Shelf border absent
3. Presque isles
4. Quondam islands (Islands in Lake
plain lowland swamp or marsh)

B. Hard Rock Islands
1. Submerged shelf
2. Submerged shelf absent
3. Presque isles

II. SUBSEQUENT ISLANDS

A. Planated islands (glacial drift planated
to water level by wave cutting)
B. Marsh, swamp and bog islands
C. Sidds (Floating mats and weed bed islands)
D. Mud flats
E. Marl islands
F. Delta islands
G. Bar and spit islands
H. Land tied islands
I. Blind and sunken islands
J. Shoal and intermittent islands
K. Stacks and chimneys

III. ARTIFICIAL ISLANDS
Made by cutting channels through marshes;
across promontories or peninsulas; and by fills,
dam impoundments, etc.

isle

With reference to lakes, the word *isle* can have much the same meaning as *island*. However, its frequency of use in place names is much less, and its range of meaning somewhat narrower. The word island is applied alike to relatively large and extremely small bodies of land; *isle* by comparison applies to relatively large bodies, but the diminutive "islet" is employed to differentiate the extremely small projections above the surface of the water. Isle is never, or rarely, applied in localisms and colloquial terms such as "sunken island"; "blind island" and "floating island".

isobath

A depth contour; a line marking equal depths in a lake or other body of water.

jetty

A structure similar to a groin but usually built in pairs. It is constructed for the purpose of preventing blocking (by sediment deposition) of a navigable passage into a harbor.

kalkgyttja

Lake bottom muds mixed more or less with calcium carbonate. (Naumann)

katavothrai (katavothron)

The hole in the bottom, or the sublacustrine outlet, which drains a sink-hole lake.

kettle lake

One occupying a constructional hollow, rudely circular in form, in Glacial drift mostly in outwash plains and moraines. The "kettle" or the "kettlehole" may be either a closed basin, or the lake in it may have an outlet.

See: *pothole*

kumatology

The science which is concerned with the phenomena of water waves.

lac

French for lake. The word appears as a generic in names of lakes (for example Lac Vieux Desert in the Upper Peninsula of Michigan) and infrequently as a common noun in parts of the United States where the influence of early French exploration and settlement remains.

Lacology

That branch of Science which is concerned with the study of lakes, ponds and all other lentic water bodies — their geologic origin and evolution; hydrography; geomorphology; biologic aspects; economic and social significance; development, use, management and conservation of water and shoreland.

Lacology, the Science of lakes, would be analogous to Potamology, the Science of rivers.

See: *Limnology*

lacuster

The central part of a lake.

lacustrian

The person dwelling in a house on or built over the water of a lake. The term applies mainly to prehistoric lake dwellers.

See: *laker*

lacustrine

As an adjective, lacustrine relates to or pertains to lakes.

lagg

Some types of peat bogs are convex; they are higher in the center and have depressed areas, sometimes covered by water, around the margins. The marginal areas have been distinguished by the Swedish word *lagg*.

lago

Italian for lake. Lago appears in a few place names, as the generic, in the United States, but does not signify any special kind of water body.

lagoon

A water body in a depression back of an offshore bar, a beach ridge or shore dune, with these geomorphic features acting as barriers or dams. Such *lagoons* are a common occurrence on sea coasts, the shores of the Great Lakes and the larger inland lakes. Lagoons along the sea coast may contain fresh, brackish or salt water and many are subject to fluctuations in the salinity of the water. Lagoon in some of its wider meanings is applied to bays or arms either completely cut-off or connected with the main body of a lake; to an estuary; and to a water feature in the nature of a slough or bayou. The term is sometimes loosely applied to any kind of artificial pond, and to any other excavation, especially if these are intended to serve some decorative purpose or are regarded as aesthetic. The term is also applied to ponds for the treatment of sewage, and disposal of farm manure, but this may be regarded as an abuse.

laguna

Spanish for lake; occasionally a term for a marsh. It
is applied to both natural and artificial water bodies in
Southwestern United States from Texas to California.

lake

The word *lake* is a common one which has been in use
over a long period of time, and one that has been given
a diversity of applications, so much so that any attempt
to sharply distinguish it from other hydronyms and give
it a very precise, limited meaning, is likely to end in fu-
tility. Definitions such as "an inland body of standing water; a body of water completely surrounded by land,"
though highly inclusive, are not quite adequate. The
word is used loosely, often interchangeably with *pond,
reservoir, sea* and other hydronyms; in usage, it is not entirely restricted to inland waters but in instances has been
applied to marine coastal waters as well; it has not been
entirely restricted to standing water, but has also been
applied to a widening in the course of a river, and to wide
connecting waterways which have a perceptible flow; it
is applied to bodies of both fresh and saline waters; to a
wide range in size, from a mere dot, an acre or so in the
landscape, to vast expanses the size of Lake Superior and
the Caspian Sea; to water contained in either a natural
basin or to that in an artificial basin; to impoundments
back of dams; to bodies of water covered with vegetation
as well as open water; to transitory bodies of water; and
to sites which were formerly lakes, but are now marsh, or
completely dessicated and literally dry, and to *paleo* water
bodies, those long extinct and existing in a past geologic
period. The word *Lake* as a part of a geographic or place
name generally carries more prestige than *Pond, Reservoir*
and some other names for water bodies, and therefore

is often preferred, and is made a replacement for previous names such as *Reservoir,* in the promotion of tourist and recreational business, and in the commercial development of shoreland for sites for homes, cottages and resorts.

lake access

A path, road or right of way over which a person may travel in order to enter upon or depart from the surface of a lake.

>See: *egress*
>*ingress*

lake association

>See: *Association*

lake basin

>See: *basin* (lake)

lake bed

>See: *bed* (lake)
>*bottom*
>*floor*

lake bottom deposits (fertilizer value)

In connection with rejuvenation of nearly extinct lakes by dredging of the bottom deposits, the question often arises — How valuable are the "muds" of lake bottoms as fertilizer? For most Michigan Lakes the value of the dredged material, in comparison with commercial fertilizer, is very low, and for distant use is not enough to warrant the cost of hauling and spreading. The phosphorus content especially in the few analyses available is in some deposits little more than a trace. Where marl is a part of the bottom deposits, this material may have a

value no greater than that of ground limestone, as an
amendment, on near-by lands. Where the bottom deposit
is largely organic, the dredgings may have a beneficial
effect, because of the nitrogen and organic matter, and
warrant the cost of spreading on nearby land, which has
soil other than peat or muck.

lake building

The construction of artificial lakes and extensive alteration of natural lakes by engineering procedures primarily
for the purpose of creating water bodies for recreation
and frontage for home sites. Artificial lakes may be created
by dams, by excavation and by diversion of water; and
natural lakes may be fused or joined into a single body,
or may be deepened by dredging.

See: *artificial*
rejuvenated lake
restored lake

lake community (ecologic)

In an ecologic sense a lake community is a particular
association of plants and animals living in lake water, on
the lake bottom or on the shore.

lake community (socio-economic)

A fixed residential community, or village with a lake
as the reason for its existence. A lake, depending on size,
may have a single community, or several, bordering its
shores.

See: *development* (lake)
resort (lake)

lake dam

A dam across the outlet of a natural lake: constructed
for the purpose of creating a reservoir for power or other
uses; for the purpose of improving the recreational value

Photo — Wisconsin Conservation Department
Dam with adjustable gate on outlet of Lac Vieux Desert, Wisconsin.

of a water body by raising or stabilizing its water level;
for preventing pollution from backwater.

See: *filter dam*

lake developer

An individual, company, corporation or governmental entity interested in the development, use or management of lake property. Natural and artificial lakes are equally susceptible to lake development.

lake directory

A mere listing of the geographic names and locations of the lakes of a geographic area.

See: *lake inventory*

lake drive

A road constructed around the lake and close to the shore for the dual purpose of providing access and enjoyment for the riparian owners. Modern planning has moved the lake drive a considerable distance inland in order to provide safe pedestrian access for cottage owners to the lake and to control trespass.

lake farming

The management of lakes for the production of crops, such as fish and other aquatic animals, and for the production of aquatic plants which have a commercial value.

lake frontage blight

Lake frontage blight is a marked deterioration in the appearance and value of shoreland development. It may result from lack of maintenance, progressive decrease in lake level, pollution or numerous other causes. Blight may occur in old exclusive high class areas from lack of maintenance or in new areas as a result of poor planning, lack of zoning or poor platting procedures.

In extreme cases, local governmental units may condemn a blighted area and clear it for renewal or alternative uses.

lake gage

An instrument used to measure the elevation of the water surface of a lake. A simple design, the staff gage, consists of a firmly placed post which has inches and feet painted on its surface. The lake level is determined by visual observation. More complex automatic recorder type gages have a float in a stilling well, which is attached by cable to the revolving drum of a recorder. The changes in elevation are automatically transcribed by pen on a chart attached to the spring or electric drive drum. A chart will normally cover a 30 day period.

lake guns

Explosive gun-like sounds, which are sporadically produced in some lakes. A possible cause of the sounds is the sudden escape of imprisoned gases produced in bottom deposits.

lake improvement cost benefit ratio

It is customary today to economically analyse proposed lake improvements by comparing the estimated cost with the estimated benefits. If the value of the benefits to the landowners is greater than the cost of the operation, the proposal may be considered to be economically sound. Problems arise when intangibles and indirect benefits are considered in the analysis.

See: *benefits*

lake inventory

A lake inventory is a listing of features of the lake itself and of the adjacent shoreland that have an economic or social use and significance. However, the "assets" of a lake, unlike the assets included in an inventory of the merchandise of a store, or the property of an estate, can-

not, in only exceptional instances, be given a specific
money value as separate items. Most so-called inventories
are only partial, and not complete evaluations of a lake,
or number of lakes, as a natural resource, in that they are
limited in the evaluations and comparisons to a single, or
one or two, items or categories, such as: beaches, bathing
and hotel accommodations; storage capacity and use for
power and industrial purposes; fish production; or wildfowl hunting. Some publications, although they carry a
few facts in addition to the names and locations of lakes,
still remain properly *directories* and so do not qualify as
inventories.

See: *economic classes of lakes and lakelands*

lake level stabilization (engineering)

As interpreted for engineering purposes, lake level stabilization includes data collection and analysis, investigation of ideal lake level, design, construction and maintenance of structures required to stabilize the lake level at
the desired elevation, most satisfactory for the majority
of riparian owners.

lake level stabilization (legal)

As a legal term, in Michigan, lake level stabilization
covers the procedure by which two-thirds of the riparian
owners or the county board of supervisors may petition
the circuit court for a lake level hearing, the hearing and
presentation of evidence and the court's decision. Once
the lake level has been stipulated by the court it remains
unchanged until a new hearing is requested. The decision
of the court (to set the legal level) does not imply that a
structure must be built but it does provide substantial
protection for those involved from subsequent independent
works by individuals or interested groups.

lake level stabilization assessment district

Under Michigan law an assessment district established by the County Board of Supervisors for the assessment of costs involved with lake level stabilization planning, construction and maintenance.

lake loam

A term which has been applied to loess, which in some locations may have been formed by deposition in lakes.

lake map

See: *lake survey*

lake marsh

A portion of the lake bottom that supports a dense growth of emergent aquatic plants. A marsh may also be designated a lake marsh when it occupies the site of a former lake.

See: *marsh lake*

Marsh occupying site of former lake; at times contains patches of open water.

lake ochre

Bacteria in some lakes, under certain conditions, are capable of precipitating ferric hydroxide. Ochreous muds as well as hard nodules and crusts of limonite have been observed on lake bottoms. Bog iron and earthy ochreous deposits are not uncommon in marshes and swamps which were formerly the sites of lakes.

lake plain

The term may be applied to the nearly flat bed of an extinct lake; or may be applied also to the flat lowland or former lake bottom bordering an existing lake.

lake regimen

An analysis of the total quantity of water involved with a lake over a designated period of time; commonly presented on an annual basis. A complete lake regimen study would provide the following information:
1. Direct precipitation on the lake surface (in inches).
2. Evaporation and sublimation losses from the lake surface (in inches).
3. Stream inflow (in cubic or acre feet).
4. Stream outflow (in cubic or acre feet).
5. Seepage losses through lake bottom (in cubic or acre feet).
6. Migration of ground water into the lake basin (in cubic or acre feet).
7. Transpiration losses by aquatic plants.
8. Water diverted from lake.
9. Water pumped or drained into lake basin

The annual water demands of riparian vegetation may also be considered as a factor in the lake regimen.

lake resort

See: *resort lake*

lake subdivision

An area of land, fronting upon or in close proximity to a lake, that is platted for sale by individual lots. Many so-called lake subdivisions include land remote from the

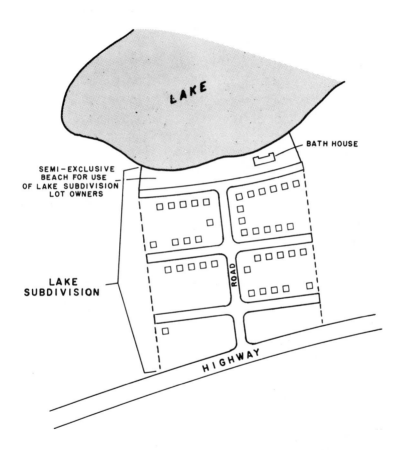

lake frontage and in such instances the owners of lots must use an exclusive or semi-exclusive access or community beach in order to enjoy the lake proper; these lots are frequently referred to as back lots.

Lake Survey

The United States Lake Survey was authorized by Congress in 1841, and placed under the direction of the Corps. of Engineers, U. S. Army. For the Great Lakes and connecting waters, the Survey provides charts which show the depths of the water and the location of features such as shoals, bars, reefs, channels and lights which pertain to navigation. In addition, the charts show the topography and geographic features of the shoreland for variable distances inland.

lake survey

A map or report depicting, describing or inventorying separately or in combination the physical, hydrographic, limnological, geographic, economic and aesthetic characteristics of a lake or group of lakes. The detail covered varies with the method and purpose of the survey.

lake use lot

A lot which is near enough to a lake for the owner to conveniently use the lake for fishing, hunting and other uses. Its location does not provide for the enjoyment of the *lakescape* but access to the lake is commonly provided.

See: *lakefront lot*
lakeview lot

lake view

See: *aesthetics*

lakeview lot

A lot which is near enough to a lake for the owner to enjoy a view of the lake. Commonly, some form of access is provided for *lakeview lot* owners.

See: *lakefront lot*
lake use lot

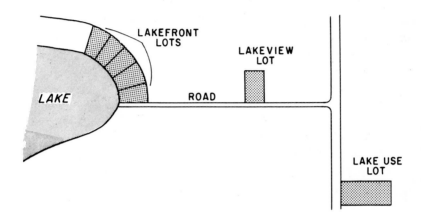

Sketch showing location of lakefront, lakeview and lake use lots.

lake vista

See: *aesthetics*

lakefront lot

Same as *front lot.*
See: *frontage*
front lots
lake use lot
lakeview lot

lakeland

(1) Land that lies within the vicinage of a lake or lakes; that which is sufficiently near for the lake, or lakes,

to have an important bearing upon its present and potential use and values.

(2) A geographic name for a district or area that contains a large number of lakes.

(3) A place name given because of location near, or association, with lakes.

lakelet

A very small lake. The word has no exact meaning in terms of size. Small bodies of water of five to ten acres or more may be casually mentioned as *lakelets;* but in another locality, and by other standards and customs a body of water no larger than one or two acres may be a *lake* and even bear a geographic name as such.

laker

Applied to a person living on the shore of, or spending a large part of his time on a lake. Also to some animal characteristically living in a lake: and to a ship engaged in commerce on a lake.

lakescape

The whole area of a lake, or any portion, its water surface, islands, shoreline features and scenery, which can be viewed from an observation point. However, very small bodies of water may be considered merely as elements or components of a *landscape.*

land (water covered)

See: *submerged land*

land lake

A kind of intermittent lake. The basin contains water for a period and subsequently becomes dry land. In some locations the bottoms of such lakes are used for the production of cultivated crops during the dry periods.

landing

In lumbering in some northern states, the term *landing* was given to the place on the bank of a lake or river where logs, cut in the winter, were hauled and piled, and, in spring, rolled into the water to be floated to the saw mills. A few of the old landings remain as present day place names.

The term *landing* may also refer to a place on a lake shore which has facilities for taking on and discharging passengers and freight carried by boats; or the *landing* may be merely a convenience for pleasure boats, and a boat livery.

landlocked bay

A bay whose water has been completely separated from the main body of the lake by a bar.

landlocked lake

One that has no surface effluent, in contrast to one that has an outflowing stream whose waters eventually reach the sea.

Many small lakes are completely enclosed by marsh, bog or swamp, and apparently do not have an outlet stream. However, if the individual basin in which they are located has an outlet stream such marsh or bog lakes are not landlocked.

See: *drainage lake*
seepage lake

landmark (lake)

A prominent land feature or structure that is easily

recognizable from a great distance over a lake surface. Landmarks are useful reference points for people who boat on large bodies of water.

landslide lakes

A landslide sometimes flows across and fills a stream valley sufficiently to create a dam and a lake. Numerous examples of lakes of this origin can be cited in mountain regions.

lateral lake

A kind of fluviatile lake. A large stream carrying a heavy load of sediment may build up its bed and banks at a much faster rate than its tributaries. Sediments so built up form embankments or levees which impound the water of the tributary or lateral, thus forming a lake.

launching area

An area on the shore of a lake, usually at the end of a public access way, designed for the launching of boats

from trailers. Some launching sites are provided with paved ramps extending into the water. The lack of adequate parking facilities for cars and trailers often limits the capacity of use of the launching area.

Laurentian lakes

A geographic name for the group of great lakes drained by the St. Lawrence River.

Laurentian Divide (Height of Land)

The surface watershed boundary or divide in Canada separating those lakes and streams flowing into the Great Lakes and St. Lawrence River from those lakes and streams flowing northward to the Hudson Bay.

law of inverse use, lake

The relative use of lake water and beach does not bear a direct relation to the increase in population of a lake community.

leatherleaf bog

See: *bog lake*

lee shore

The shore which lies in the direction of the prevailing winds. It is thus protected from strong wave action, and is often the swampy shore.

legal level

A level set by court decree. In Michigan in cases where the lake level is subject to control by engineering measures, the county board of supervisors or two thirds of the riparians may petition the circuit court to set a legal level for a lake. After proper notice and hearing the court stipulates a legal level that appears most serviceable for those concerned. After a legal level is set no modification of the lake level is permitted unless directed towards establishment or maintenance of the legal level as set by the court.

legal reliction
Land between established legal level and the high water mark. This would apply only when the legal level lies below the natural high water mark.

length (of a lake)
See: *breadth* for illustration
The shortest distance on the water surface between the most distant points on the lake shoreline.

lentic (lenitic) waters
The term, *lentic* pertains to lakes or ponds or to any body of *standing water*.
In contrast, the term *lotic* applies to any body of moving, or flowing, water such as a river or other stream. However, all bodies of water occurring in nature, or artificial, do not fit neatly into one or the other group. According to local usage of terms some bodies of water which have perceptible current and flow may still retain the name *lake* or *pond* and conversely some which have scarcely a perceptible current, or flow, may still retain the name *river*. Neither of the terms lentic or lotic aptly applies to tidal waters.

levee lakes
Lakes related in their origin to river bank levees. Rivers tend to build natural levees on their banks by the deposition of sediments from the initial overflow of flood waters,

and in the case of large streams especially such as the Mississippi, these may reach such proportions that they act as barriers or enclosures to hold water other than the river and to form lakes. Some of the specific kinds of levee lakes recognized are: lateral levee lakes; crescentic levee lakes; delta levee lakes.

level (of a lake)

The elevation of the water surface above or below a datum. Where authoritative bench marks are available, elevations are commonly given with reference to sea level. A figure for the elevation of a Great Lake is usually one for the mean level, or the ordinary high water mark. The levels (elevations) most frequently quoted for inland lakes are from United States Geological Survey Topographic sheets and in reality represent the lake levels at the time of field survey. The actual elevation at a particular time might be above or below a recorded elevation depending upon the fluctuations to which the lake is subject.

See: *legal level*
stage

level ditch

See: *blast hole* for illustration

A ditch or canal-like excavation in marsh or other wetland. The purpose is to increase the area of open water and provide game corridors, rather than to provide drainage, since the "ditch" is without drop or gradient.

liman

A European term for an estuarine brackish or salt water lagoon.

limeweed

An old popular name for pondweeds, certain species of the genus *Potamogeton* which characteristically grow in hard water lakes and have crusts of lime (calcium carbonate) on their stems and leaves.

limited access (lake)

Access to the water surface for all riparians at a single place. Except for this limited access location the lake shore remains natural and unchanged.

limnetic zone

In lakes partly occupied by emergent vegetation, the *limnetic zone* is the area of open water.

limnokrene

A term for a lake, or pool, formed by a spring.

See: *spring lake*

Photo – Michigan Tourist Council

Kitchitikipi Spring, near Manistique, Michigan.

Limnology

The science which deals with lakes, and by extension with all inland waters. It is concerned especially with the biology of the waters and bottoms.

See: *Lacology*

linn (lin)

An old word of Gaelic origin for a pool, especially one into which a cataract falls.

litigious littoral

In the physiographic evolution of a lake from open water to dry land, the shoreline, or marginal waters of the lake may be first to be covered by aquatic vegetation and otherwise filled in and reduced to a marshy condition,

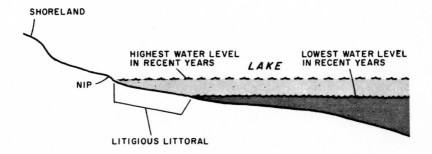

especially where a shallow submerged shelf or a shallow sheltered bay is present. The status of these transitional areas, whether they are to be regarded as shoreland or whether they remain as a part of the lake proper, is sometimes a matter of contention and litigation because such matters as riparian rights, ownership and use of the areas in question are involved.

See: *purgatorial reliction*
reliction
riparian rights
shoreline

littoral

See: *beach profile* for illustration

The word pertains to the shore, either or both the shoreland and shore water and near shore bottom of a lake. *Littoral* is also a name for the shoreland for an indeterminate distance back from the water but as such is pretty much restricted to sea coasts. *Littoral* in a limnological sense, refers to shallow water in which aquatic vegetation can be present on the bottom, as contrasted with deep water or the *profundal.*

See: *profundal bottoms*
sublittoral
zonation

littoral currents

Pertaining to lakes, the currents alongside, or parallel, to the shore.

littoral drift

The material that moves in the littoral zone under the influence of waves and currents.

littoral plants

Littoral plants are those growing on or near the shore.

See: *littoral*

littoral property

Sometimes used as a synonym for riparian property.

See: *riparian rights*

littoral shelf

See: *beach profile* for illustration

A shallow submerged shelf, or terrace, extending lakeward from the water line of a beach. Where a cliff or high bank, rises from the water line and is subject to the erosive action of waves, the cliff recedes under wave attack, and a terrace of cutting, by waves, and of deposition, by currents, is gradually formed and often extends outward a considerable distance from shore, ending in deep water with a steep front or "drop-off." The beach may be regarded as the part of the shelf which lies above the water level. Also called: *subaqueous terrace, submerged terrace; submerged platform; cut and built terrace; wave-cut terrace; wave-built terrace; sublacustrine shelf.*

littoral zone

A narrow zone including both the land and water immediately bordering the shoreline.

See: *zoning*

lobe (of a lake)

The word *lobe* is sometimes used as a common noun in descriptions, and also as a proper noun, a part of a geographic name, for a longish rounded segment in the nature of a *bay* or *arm*.

loch, lough

Respectively Scottish and Irish words for lake.

logan

An old localism in Maine for a bay, inlet, pocket or sheet of water in a swamp. The word is probably related to the Indian words *penelogan* and *peneloken*. The word *peneloken* has been applied in Wisconsin to a bay or inlet of a lake.

longshore currents

Currents near or *along* the shore. These currents may transport and deposit the finer matter of the detritus of wave erosion. Means about the same as *littoral currents.*

loop bar

Where a spit has a pronounced hook at its end, and this continues to grow until it reaches the shore, a *loop bar* is formed.

looped bar

One that is arched or curved in contrast to the usual straight line feature.

See: *bar*

loosetrife

One of the aquatic plants to which the popular name loosestrife is applied is *Decodon verticillatus,* a shrubby herbaceous plant, common on the margins of lakes in bogs and marshes. Its peculiar habit of growth enables it to advance out over the open water, and it is often a pioneer in the formation of a floating bog mat. Its dense tangle of vegetation makes a "false" shoreline.

lot-water ratio (of a lake)

The total water acreage equated to a single riparian lot. If there are 100 riparian lots, the "lot-water ratio" would be 1:1/100 of total area.

lotic

See: *lentic*

lough

See: *loch*

lows and balls

In localities along sea coasts offshore submarine ridges (balls) and depressions (lows) of sand parallel to the shoreline have been given this descriptive name. On the coast of Lake Michigan, long, offshore sublacustrine ridges of sand parallel and conforming to the curves of the shoreline, have been reported. Possibly the term could be appropriately applied here. However, for the inland lakes of Michigan, it is unlikely that any conditions exist to which the term *lows* and *balls* could be properly applied.

maar

See: *crater lake*

made land (lake shore)

In its most commonly accepted meaning, *made land* is *man made*, or artificial as opposed to natural land. The term with this connotation was given a kind of technical standing, about 1910, by the U. S. Bureau of Soils when it was made to designate a unit of mapping in Soil Surveys.

On lake shores, *made land* generally consists of fills on marshy borders, or in shallow lake bottoms bordering the shore line, but may include any kind of artificial surface, resulting from man's activities, which has replaced a natural surface.

Land may be made by natural processes such as delta deposition, formation of bars, beach drift, the formation of dunes, changes in lake level, and deposition by river floods in the case of fluviatile lakes, but such *made lands* are usually known under the terms *accretion, reliction,* and *alluvion.*

See: *fill*

man-property value ratio (lake)

The current dollar value of riparian land and development equated to a single riparian. If there are 100 riparians the "man-property value ratio" would be 1:1/100 of total value of riparian land and development.

man-water ratio (lake)

The ratio between the number of persons using the water at any specified time and the area (expressed in acres) of lake surface. A measure of the intensity of use.

See: *cottage-water ratio*

marais

This term meaning a marsh or spread of shallow water was given to wet land features by early French explorers and later French-Canadians, and remains as an element in place names in several localities in Michigan and other parts of the United States.

margin (lake)

The land immediately bordering the water line of a lake.

See: *marginal waters*

marginal lake

Referring to glacial origin — one formed by dams along the margin of an ice front.

marginal waters (of a lake)

The lake water close to the shoreline.

marina (lake)

A commercial establishment, located on lake shores or extending into a lake, for the business of servicing boats;

Photo — *Michigan Tourist Council*

Marina at Traverse City, Michigan.

analogous to a garage. Municipal marinas are basins providing mooring for boats; also some *marinas* afford storage for boats and hotel accommodations for the boat owners.

marine railway portage

See: *portage*

marl (in lakes)

A form of calcium carbonate which occurs commonly as a bottom deposit in hard water lakes; and as a deposit underlying marshes, bogs, and swamps which occupy the sites of former, or extinct lakes. It occurs mostly as soft mudlike grayish or off-white masses, but locally may be composed in part of hard crusts and hard concretions. It

Marl being excavated for agricultural use. ——————

Lake ——————

may be nearly pure calcium carbonate, or may contain magnesium carbonate and extraneous impurities as clay, sands and organic matter in small or large proportions. In many Michigan lakes it has been the chief source of natural filling, accumulating in some locations to as much as 30 to 40 feet in thickness. Marl can have an important influence on the flora and fauna, on the recreational use and the commercial development of a lake. Marl is also known as *bog-lime*.

marl biscuit

Flattish, rounded, hard concretions of marl; often found on the shallow bottoms and strands of hard water lakes. The lime has been secreted by certain species of algae into rounded masses (often with a fragment of shell or

(Black and white divisions on ruler = 2 inches.)

other matter as a nucleus) usually not more than 1 to 3 inches in diameter, but in rare instances to as much as 6 inches. After the original soft algal masses harden, they may be modified by wave action. Also known as *lake biscuits*.

marl lake

One characterized by large quantities of marl in its bottom deposits. Where the marl bottom is white, not covered by organic muds, the water is often remarkably clear, or on the other hand "milky" where shallows are subject to wave action. The term "marl lake" has been applied also to a lake which has been mined, or dredged, as a commercial source of marl especially for the manufacture of Portland cement.

marl shoal

See: *shoal*

marlite (marlyte)

A petrologic term for marl in a hardened form. Numerous lakes contain semi-indurated encrustations, fragments, nodules, "biscuits" and pebbles of marl on their bottoms and shores. *Marlite* may be extended in meaning to include such material.

marsh

Marsh is commonly differentiated from *swamp* on the basis of its herbacious vegetation — grasses, sedges, reeds, etc., in contrast to the tree vegetation of swamps. Marshes may be "dry" and intermittently water covered or they may be permanently water covered. In Michigan, marsh for the most part occurs in basins, the sites of former lakes, or as lake border lowland. In the evolution of lakes from open water to land, they may pass through a marsh stage, and for certain early transitions, it becomes an arbitrary decision whether they be called watery marshes or "grass lakes."

Fresh water marshes are sometimes divided into two groups; *shallow* and *deep*, by wildlife specialists. The distinction is an arbitrary one based upon the depth to which the marsh surface is ordinarily covered by water such as shallow, no more than six inches; and deep, six inches to three feet or more. Management of marsh land may include structures to regulate or restore water levels.

See: *grass lakes*

marsh lake

(1) An open water lake located in a marsh, and surrounded by wide expanses of marsh land. (2) A lake more or less completely covered by emergent vegetation, especially sedge and grasses.

marsh shore

Lake borderland consisting of marsh extending to the water line. Often the marsh vegetation and the emergent

Sedge marsh on margin of a sand plain lake. Photo — Davis, C. A., *Peat*, 1907, Michigan Geological Survey, Lansing, Michigan. (page 196)

aquatic vegetation of the lake merge in a manner that makes the precise location of a shoreline difficult or arbitrary. A marsh shore is usually classified as a "soft shore".

See: *marsh lake*

massive lakes

The descriptive term "massive" has been applied to
lakes having an enormous volume, such as the Great
Lakes of the U. S. and Lake Baikal in Siberia.

Massive is often employed in geographic descriptions
as a comparative — a lake that has greater depth and
volume, and therefore greater mass of water, than another
is "more massive", or a group may be separated as the
"more massive lakes".

mature shoreline

One that is relatively smooth or regular in form; one
on which the original headlands and re-entrants have been
largely obliterated by natural development processes.

meadow (lake)

In common usage, where the term "meadow" is applied to natural borderland of lakes, it usually refers to
shallow grass marsh in contrast to swampy and other
wooded shores. Meadow as a popular term is also occasionally applied to extensive beds of vegetation growing
on the bottom of clear water lakes.

See: *beaver meadow*

mean depth

The volume of a lake divided by its surface area. Also
called reduced thickness.

See: *volume*

mean highwater level

The elevation at the margin of the area occupied by
water during a time period. A nip, or scarp, on the shore
made by the action of waves is usually present at this
level. Or the position of the mean high water line might

be marked by the change from aquatic to terrestrial vegetation. Where a legal boundary needs to be established for a lake, the mean level may be accepted. In some court decisions this has been made the legal boundary of a lake.
See: *highwater mark*

meander corner

In the General Land Office Survey, the point where a township or section line intersects a meanderable body of water. The monument established at such intersection is called a "meander corner".

meander land

Unsurveyed land representing lake bottom lying between the present water line, of a lake, and the original shore line as shown by General Land Office Survey meander lines. Such land may be designated relicted, but reliction is recognized on non-meandered lakes as well as on meandered ones.
See: *meandered lake*
reliction

meandered lake

In the General Land Office Survey, a meandered lake is one whose shoreline was traversed and its sinuosities located. When a lake was meandered its water surface area was segregated from the public domain and was not open to patent. In the plan of the Survey, it was the intent to meander all lakes 25 acres or more in size, however in practice the intent was not always observed.

The meandered lake has a recognized weight as evidence in legal decisions where lake waters, shore line lands and reliction are involved. However, in the General Land Office Survey, only certain selected lakes had their shorelines meandered, and those not so surveyed are referred to as *non-meandered* lakes.

meander line

The traverse of the margin of a permanent natural body of water. The meander line of a lake as established by the General Land Office was supposed to correspond to the mean high water mark of the lake. These meander lines are not regarded as land boundary lines because lakes are subject to fluctuations and permanent changes in level, and the riparian presumably owns to the water line wherever that may be.

meander scrolls

The meander channels of large rivers often migrate leaving behind a series of arcuate ridges and troughs, called scrolls. The ridges are produced by outer bank erosion and inner bank deposits. Bodies of standing water often occur in the troughs.

median line (of a lake)

In concept the median line is the line all points of which are equidistant from the nearest points on opposite shores. The median line can be important as a boundary line between states and nations; and minor governmental units; and as a line limiting control of ownership of lake bottom and surface water between riparian owners on opposite shores.

See: *boundary lake*
　　center (of a lake)

mere

In England, *mere* is a term for a sheet of standing water especially in the *fens*. In the United States, *mere* appears in the sense of *marais* and *marsh,* but only rarely, if at all, as part of a place name for a body of water, such as a lake or pond except in literary or poetic usage.

merl (merle)

A vernacular word common in southern Michigan during the early period of settlement used to describe *marl lakes.*

meromictic lake

A lake in which some of the water remains unmixed with the main water mass during the circulation periods. The deep stagnant layer of a meromictic lake has been designated as the *monimolimnion* and the part in which circulation can occur as the *mixolimnion.* The boundary between these two parts is known as the *chemocline.*

mesotrophic lake

One that is intermediate in fertility; neither notably high nor notably low in its total productivity. Intermediate between oligotrophic and eutrophic.

See: *eutrophic lake*
oligotrophic lake

metalimnion

The thermocline.

metes and bounds lot

An irregular lot fronting upon or adjacent to a lake which is surveyed, described and located by established bench marks or natural features. During the early develop-

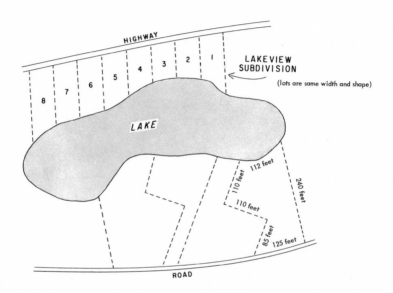

METES AND BOUNDS LOT

mental stages on a lake, the original owner may be encouraged to sell off certain select lots to buyers who have predetermined needs or desires. Usually, *metes and bounds lots* are irregular in shape and size as compared with regular platted lots.

midges

Tiny insects, species of Chironomids, called blind mosquitoes. The larvae are bloodworms. Midges sometimes breed in enormous numbers in lakes, especially those rich in organic matter or those that have been polluted by sewage effluent and support a prolific growth of algae. Midges can be a serious pest on lake shores; they enter the eyes and nose of a person and sometimes are in such dense numbers that they are a menace to traffic.

mill lake

In Michigan any lake that had a sawmill on it was commonly designated as a mill lake. Logs were frequently floated to the mill and stored within a chain boom near the mill jack ladder.

mill pond

A relatively small impoundment, usually back of a

Photo – Michigan Conservation Department

Sawmill pond.

man-made dam, used to supply power for the operation of a mill, usually a flour, or grist mill. However, in northern Michigan MILL POND has been applied as a name for ponds used in connection with lumber mills and mines. Commonly the water body remains and the name is retained even though the water is no longer used for its original purpose.

Under some circumstances where an old mill pond has become clogged with aquatic vegetation, it may be a source of foul odors in midsummer, a breeding place for mosquitoes, and therefore properly condemned as a nuisance.

mineral rights (bottom land)

In Michigan, the riparian owner (or riparians) owns all rights, title and interest to the minerals underlying the lake bottom; muck and peat are considered to be minerals.

Certain other states claim ownership of these minerals by virtue of their perpetual ownership of the lake bottom.

Also, ownership of the lake bottom, whether or not vested in the State may hinge upon the interpretation of "navigable" as applied to the lake.

mire

The word *mire* occasionally appears as a term for wetland features and usually has about the same implication as the terms *bog* and *marsh*.

mirror lakes

The surface of a lake can reflect light rays, and on some particular lakes the images of reflection from a smooth surface, shoreland scenery and clouds, are unusually aesthetic. Such lakes are called mirror lakes and often are so designated in the geographic name.

Photo – Michigan Conservation Department

A mirror lake in Northern Michigan.

mixolimnion

That part of a *meromictic* lake in which circulation can occur.

See: *meromictic lakes*

moat

An old term used in New England for an ox-bow or river meander lake.

The term *moat* was applied to the waters in old abandoned river channels in the Mississippi flood plain by N. S. Shaler (Tenth Ann. Rept U.S. Geol. Surv. Part I, 1888-89, page 277).

moat lake

The term *moat* is applied to lakes, usually in a stage of senescence, characterized by a peripheral, or outer, ring

A small moat lake.

of water enclosing a filled interior. A number of such lakes have been observed in Michigan, especially in pot holes containing bogs.

moored boat
A boat used at one location or on a single body of water during an entire recreational season. They are launched at the beginning of the season and when not in use are moored at a permanent location.

See: *transient boat*
fleet boats

mole
A breakwater.

See: *breakwater*

monimolimnion
The bottom non-circulating layer of water in a lake.

morainal dam lakes
Glacial lakes, in valleys, lying back of drift dams, formed as the glacier, occupying the valley, receded. Some lakes of this origin are associated with existing glaciers.

morainal lakes
Glacial lakes in depressions, or basins, which resulted from the irregular deposition of the drift in terminal and ground moraines.

morass
An inclusive term for swamp, marsh, bog and other water covered land. The term was so used by N. S. Shaler, Fresh Water Morasses of the United States, 10th Ann. Rept. U. S. Geol. Survey, 1888-1889, parts. pages 261-339.

However, in present day literature, *morass* is largely restricted to literary expression.

morphometry
Lake measurements such as: area, depth, length, width, volume, shoreline, bottom gradients.

mortlake
The term *mortlake* has been used in England as the equivalent of an abandoned river channel or ox-bow type of lake, but in the United States, no instance of its use, applied to a water feature can be cited.

See: *moat*

most probable number of coliform bacteria
One of the standard laboratory tests for water quality involves the determination of the most probable number of coliform bacteria per unit of water; per liter, per 100cc, per 10cc, or per cc.

This is a relatively quick, easy and cheap test to estimate the presence of coliform bacteria in water samples, especially for raw drinking water supply and at swimming beaches. Standards have been established by public health agencies to regulate public water supply systems, swimming beaches and pools. If the test indicates that coliform bacteria are present, then pathogenic bacteria and viruses could also be present. Water used for drinking purposes, without treatment should have *no* coliform present.

As pollution and smirchment of water bodies increases in intensity, this old, well accepted test is no longer adequate for current needs. It is necessary to conduct more complex, time consuming and expensive tests to actually determine the identity of the bacteria present; fecal and non-fecal. The presence of fecal bacteria represents a much greater threat to public health than coliform bacteria.

movable freehold

Lake bottom exposed by recession of the shoreline may be regarded as land that belongs to the adjoining riparian. Where such bottom land is subject to strong change in area, by emergence and submergence, according to changes in lake level it has been called, a "movable freehold".

See: *purgatorial reliction*

M.P.N.

Abbreviation for most probable number of coliform bacteria per unit of water.

See: *most probable number*

muck (lake bottom)

Muck, or the descriptive term *mucky*, is often applied to lake bottom deposits. The material so-called is usually blackish, fine in texture and composed largely of organic matter. However, the word *muck* has no precise connotation and has been applied to bottom material differing widely in physical and chemical composition.

See: *peat*

mud flats

The bare flat bottoms of lakes, largely filled by organic deposits, freshly exposed by a drop in lake level. Unless again covered by water by a restoration of former levels, such "flats" are soon converted into marsh.

Mud flat exposed by recent drop in lake level.

mud lakes

In reference to Michigan lakes, the bottom deposits commonly called "mud" are mainly organic, and are blackish or brownish, soft, mushy or slimy and colloidal in nature. Only infrequently is the "mud" of "mud lakes" inorganic clay and silt.

See: *clay, lake bottom*

multiple use lake

When applied to water bodies, multiple use has traditionally implied that management could include more than one major category of use; flood control, hydro-electric power generation, navigation, irrigation, recreation and water supply.

Due to space demands, conflicts of interest and the intense competition of various recreational uses for lake waters, multiple use is being applied in a somewhat different sense. A lake may be classified as a multiple use lake if it is managed for fishing and water skiing. *(Refer to economic classes of lakes and lakelands* for other recreational uses.) Lakeshore activities are included as lake uses. On many lakes, the surface water has been zoned on a time or spatial basis to facilitate multiple use.

See: *carrying capacity* (recreational)

muskeg lake

See: *bog lake*

muskrat house

A conical or rounded mound usually constructed of cattail, bulrush or other vegetation by muskrats in shallow lakes and in "deep" marsh. The house serves as a multiple

Muskrat house in cattail pond.

use shelter, breeding place and for food storage during the entire year. Access to these houses is usually underwater and the water must be sufficiently deep to provide access in the winter time. Also called "cabins" in Ohio and Illinois.

names of lakes

In Michigan, the Indians had given names to a large number of lakes, mainly the large ones, before the advent of the white man. A comparatively small number of the original Indian names have survived, in some modified form, but others were never accepted, or if accepted, were later abandoned, probably mainly because of difficulties in spelling and pronunciation. With the coming, in large numbers, of settlers in the southern part of the State, and with the occupation and exploration of the northern part by lumbermen and mining companies, the thousands of unnamed lakes and ponds, were rapidly given some sort of appellation for the purpose of geographic identification. No statutory rules existed in this early period (and for that matter none exists at present) pertaining to the naming of natural features. The result was a kind of anarchy in naming. Probably the greater number were given personal names, surnames and Christian, after owners of adjacent land, early explorers, land surveyors, and prominent persons of the time. A few were given the names of Indian chiefs, and tribal names. Many of the names were commonplace and unimaginative, based on shape, size, character of the water and lake bottom, associated vegetation and aquatic animals, and the result has been endless duplication of such names as Round, Long, Clear, Mud, Pine, Bass, Perch, Beaver, etc. The existing name often has little value for the purpose of geographic identification in the State. No rules were ever followed by common consent, so that naming often appears to be without logic or consistency. In some instances two or more closely associated, but separate, lakes have been given a single lake name, and on the other hand divisions of a single body of water have been given separate lake names. In most instances the specific name precedes the generic, but where the opposite obtains, no rule appears to have been followed. Likewise, the reason for the selection of the generic, whether Lake or Pond, or Reservoir, Basin, Flooding and Flowage, often is not apparent.

The names of some particular lakes have been long accepted, and so firmly established, that they are not likely to be changed or replaced. However, in many instances, old and long accepted names have been changed for various reasons. Lake names may be "official" for the reason that they have been given approval by the Board of Geographic Names, Washington, D. C., but the "official" name is not always universally observed or respected.

Due to their uniqueness and recreational appeal, many of the abandoned Indian names are now being revived to replace more recent names.

THE USUAL PROCEDURE FOR CHANGING
LAKE NAMES IN MICHIGAN IS AS FOLLOWS:

(1) Have the County Board of Supervisors pass a resolution favoring and approving the proposed change in name. This resolution must mention each lake or stream separately, stating:

- (a) Name or names by which the lake or stream is now known
- (b) Location by section, township and range
- (c) The proposed name
- (d) Reason that the proposed name is considered necessary or advisable
- (e) Meaning of name (Why so named?)
- (f) Attach a map or township plat and indicate the lake or stream affected

This information must be furnished with accuracy and completeness in order to avoid confusion and misapplication of names.

(2) Have the County Clerk send to Michigan Committee on Geographic Names, Geological Survey Division, Department of Conservation, Lansing, Michigan, a certified copy of the County Board of Supervisor's resolution of approval on the attached forms with map or township plat showing the particular lake or stream affected.

(3) The State Committee on Geographic Names will then consider and act on the proposed named or names as approved in the County Board's resolution. If the State Committee concurs with the County Board in its action, that Committee will forward the certified copy of the County Board's resolution and map or plat together with its recommendations to the U. S. Geographic Board, Washington, D.C. for that Board's consideration.

See: *official name*

narrows (lake)

A constriction in the width of a lake resulting in a comparatively narrow water passage, or strait, connecting two lobes, arms or segments of water. According to local usage, the dimensions are indefinite; the term may apply to a passage a few feet wide, or to one a few hundred feet wide.

The term is also applied to a narrow channel between two islands.

navigable (inland lakes)

The meanings of *navigable* have been determined, pretty largely, by statutes and court decisions and, therefore, have variations in time and place, accordingly. Navigability is not necessarily restricted to deep open unobstructed waters, and passage of large vessels engaged in trade, but on the contrary, in some instances very shallow lakes, with water barely deep enough to float a saw-log, a canoe or a row boat may have been declared *navigable*.

Because the interpretation of "navigable" can have a bearing upon the ownership (public versus private) of lake bottom land; upon public access and use of waters; and because of the questions and involvements which arise when rules are applied to landlocked lakes and to interstate lakes, the meaning of the word in individual cases is likely to be determined by legal argument and court decisions. The Federal test of *navigability*, briefly stated, is whether the water at time of statehood was used as a highway for boats or other vessels engaged in commerce or was capable of being so used. Some individual States have set up their own rules of navigability and meanings of *"navigable"*.

A state that claims ownership of its navigable waters may in some cases, continue ownership of a non-navigable lake. The lake may have become non-navigable because of filling by vegetation or other causes, leaving no open water, but ownership remains with the state, if the lake was "navigable" at the time the state was admitted to the Union.

Where ownership (state versus private) of the lake bottom, or submerged land, hinges upon the interpretation of *"navigable"*, the meaning of the word, and whether or not a particular lake is navigable in fact, (has water deep enough, or the water body is capable of being deepened, to permit the movement of boats engaged in trade) is likely to be determined by legal argument and judicial decisions, especially where the bottom land has assumed a high value.

necfluve (lake)

There are numerous examples of chains and trains of lakes, in basins and valleys floored with swamp or marsh, in which the individual lakes are connected by natural water channels. Some connecting waters may be very short and straight, some fairly long, narrow thread-like and winding. In some locations they may be called creeks or rivers, but they are not such in the usual sense because they have no drainage basin, no tributaries, no alluvial flood plains. For these connecting waters the term "nec-fluve" is proposed.

neck (of land; of water)
A non-technical term occasionally applied to a lake feature — either a narrow promontory or peninsula jutting out into a lake; or less often to a narrow arm of water between two promontories.

nekton
A term employed by limnologists and ecologists for the group of organisms (larger than plankton) which swim freely in the water. *Nekton* includes fishes.

neoshoreline
See: *beach profile* for illustration
environment for illustration
New shoreline; the existing shoreline which marks a change from a former level, or older shoreline; usually a recession, or lower water level.
See: *eoshoreline*

neuston
The group of organisms associated with the surface film of the water.

newland lakes
See: *consequent lakes*

nip (lake shore)
See: *beach profile* for illustration
The wave cut bank on a recession shore line. The height of the *nip* marks the difference between the level of the

existing lake and the level of its most recent higher stage. On most of the inland lakes the *nip* is only weakly developed, because in those instances where a shallow bottom slopes gently from the shore the erosive power of the waves is greatly retarded; because only small differences in level may exist between that of the lake and the most recent shore bench or terrace; and because on many lakes, water levels are unstable or greatly fluctuating. On lakes completely surrounded by marsh or bog (those in the process of extinction by the advancing vegetation) often nips are not present.

nitrogen trap

Lakes, marshes and swamps effectively remove a large percentage of the dissolved nitrogen from inflowing water. As a result of the nitrogen being fixed by aquatic vegetation the outflowing water has a lower concentration of nitrogen and other nutrients.

nitrogenous wastes

Wastes of animal or plant origin which contain a significant concentration of available nitrogen. Excessive enrichment of lakes by nitrogenous wastes (for example, sewage effluent) represents one of the most serious threats to these valuable water resources in the United States.

non-wetting sand

Sand that possesses the peculiar characteristic of resisting infiltration of water. This sand in an open container may be immersed in water without becoming saturated and globules of this sand will float upon a water surface, for long periods of time.

This term is also applied to tightly packed lenses, consisting of sand particles angular in shape and varying in size, that resist infiltration.

See: *ropey sand*

non-meandered lake

See: *meandered lake*

non-polluted (lake)

See: *pollution*

The Northwest Angle

A peninsula in the Lake of the Woods which is connected to Canadian territory but is a part of the State of Minnesota. It is necessary to traverse over Canadian territory or travel by boat in order to gain access to this peninsula. Locally it is referred to as the Northwest Angle.

nova lakes

New lakes; an inclusive term for those appearing suddenly on sites where no lakes previously existed; and also

A nova lake, Yellow Dog Plains, Marquette County, Michigan

on sites of extinct lakes. Water bodies may appear suddenly, or accumulate in a very short period of time, from such causes as: sudden collapse of roofs of caverns or underground stream channels forming sink holes; from the plugging of outlets to subterranean channels; to the damming of underground streams; dams made by landslides; land subsidence following earthquakes; abandoned channels and aggradation following river floods, storm wave erosion on beaches and lake shores; and changes in ground water levels. Nova lakes may be transitory or relatively permanent in nature.

number (of lakes)

The number of lakes especially for a region, or a State containing a large number such as Michigan, Wisconsin and Minnesota, can have considerable geographic significance, if supplemented by information about size groups and their distribution. However, the figures for numbers from different sources or compiled at different times are rarely in accordance (in fact they may exhibit wide disparity), because of lack of agreement as to what constitutes a *lake,* completeness or incompleteness of inventories, and differences and errors by individuals in the interpretation of maps and aerial photos.

observation raft

A raft-like structure provided, usually as a tourist attraction, for the observation of fauna, flora and bottom features of large deep springs and clear water lakes.

ochre gyttja

Lake bottom mud containing a high percentage of ferric hydroxide.

O.D.

Abbreviation for oxygen demand.
See: *biochemical oxygen demand*

official name (lake)

A lake name approved by the Board of Geographic
Names, United States Department of Interior is considered
to be the official name of a lake. It is presumed that the
decisions of the board are binding upon federal agencies
issuing maps. On a state or local level, the naming of
lakes is viewed with considerable latitude and maps covering the same area frequently exhibit disagreement in
names. Property owners making plat maps for lake development appear to be completely unfettered in the choice
of names.

See: *names*

offshore

See: *beach profile* for illustration
Referring to the water side of the shore line. Hydrographic features, or objects so designated are usually near,
or only a short distance from the waterline, but also may
be quite distant.

offshore wind

Wind blowing lakeward from the land.

ojo

A Mexican word (literally eye) for very small lakes or
ponds, southwestern United States.

old lake

The term is often applied to lakes in an advanced stage
of filling by endogenic deposits; a eutrophic or dystrophic

lake. The term may also be applied to a lake exhibiting an advanced stage of physiographic shoreline development.

See: *young lake*

oligopelic

Pertaining to a bottom deposit that contains very little clay.

oligotrophic lakes

Those poorly provided with the basic nutrients required for plant and animal production.

ombrotiphic

A temporary or ephemeral pool, or pond.

onshore wind

Wind blowing from the lake toward the shore or landward.

ooze (lake bottom)

A term often used for soft, fine textured or colloidal lake bottom "muds". The "mud" is usually mainly organic in composition, but *ooze* in its usage is also often applied to fine deposits of variable composition and not necessarily organic in nature, and therefore its meaning, unless supplemented, may not be very definite.

See: *gyttja*

open lake

One with an effluent in contrast to a closed lake. Some lakes may be without surface effluents but may lose water by seepage. These are in a special sense, also *open*.

See: *closed lake*

open shore (lake)

Shoreland that is devoid of trees, or has only a sparse growth, or one that is marshy, in contrast to a shore that has a dense growth of trees or shrubs beginning at the water line.

open water (lake)

(1) The water of a lake which remains unfrozen or not covered by ice, during the winter.

(2) The water surface of a lake that is free of emergent vegetation, trees, stumps or artificial obstructions.

Water in a sense is not "open" water when dense masses of submerged plants at very shallow depths interfere with boating and fishing.

In Canada, the south end of Lake of the Woods is described as "open water" in contrast to the north end which is studded with thousands of islands. House boats are not seaworthy enough to operate in the south end but are being used in the north end where the numerous islands provide shelter and unlimited safe anchorage.

ordinary high water mark

See: *beach profile* for illustration
high water mark

oriented lakes

Lakes that have an orderly spatial arrangement; the longer axes of individual lakes of a group are nearly parallel. Some of the thaw or permafrost lakes of the tundra of Alaska are definitely oriented.

outer beach

That zone of a sandy beach which is ordinarily dry, and is reached only by the waves of violent storms.

outfall

A term used for the end of a pipe, ditch, drain or distributor that carries an effluent into a lake or stream. The outfall is located on the bottom of the lake or stream to

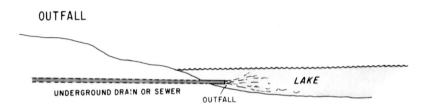

facilitate mixing of warmer, lighter effluent. Even though these structures are buried or underwater, their presence is easily determined by the odor, color, turbidity, foam and flotsam near the *outfall*. If the effluent is sewage, the bottom will have a luxuriant growth of algae or aquatic plants due to the enrichment of the water.

outflow

A synonym for *outlet* where the latter means the place where the water flows out of the lake. A discharge from the lake.

outlet (lake)

The opening from which water is discharged into an outflowing stream or other body of water. In usage, *outlet*, also is the outflowing stream itself. The term itself has little hydrologic or economic significance unless the kinds or conditions are specified: intermittent; dammed; perennial; navigable; artificial. In some lakes the *outlet* is no more than a short connecting channel with another lake or a nearby river, and in the case of a fluvial lake, *outlet* is often merely the narrowing continuation of the stream.

Generally lakes have only a single natural outlet, but exceptional instances have been noted where two or more outflowing streams are present. In the case of some river plain lakes, the outflow may be reversed during flood periods so that the *outlet* becomes temporarily, an *inlet*.

Some lakes have subaqueous outlets, that discharge through openings in their bottoms.

> See: *dual drainage lakes*
> *effluent*
> *inlet*
> *quondam outlet*

outlet head

The place where the water leaves the lake and enters the outflowing stream, or *effluent*.

outlot, lake subdivision

The owners of riparian tracts frequently reserve part of their land when subdividing, in order to capitalize upon higher future prices. Land withheld from a partially platted tract may be designated as an outlot.

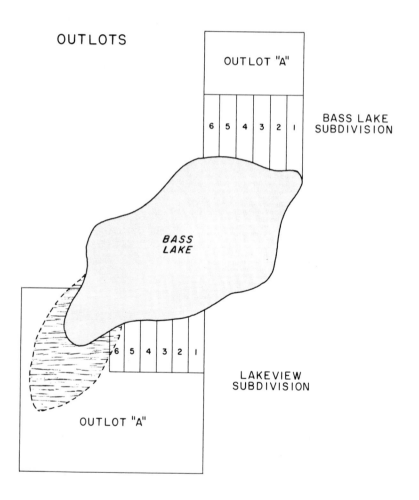

outside pond

This term is applied to water bodies in the outermost extensions of the delta of the Mississippi River. The waters

so designated appear to have been enclosed or partly so
by deposition of sediment from bifurcating distributaries
of the river, and are for the most part connected with the
Gulf. In this same setting ponds lying inland from the
delta front, and with freshened water, are called *inside
ponds*, although the distinction between the two and the
features simply called *ponds* does not always appear to be
consistent.

over-developed lake

As an economic entity, or in its social significance, a
lake is over-developed, when the number of residents on its
water frontage and the adjacent shoreland, or the amount
of resort or commercial development, and use of beaches
is out of proportion to the area and volume of water in
the lake. The use is in excess of the natural *carrying capacity*. The usual results are: conflicts of interest in use of
land and water from overcrowding; pollution; and decline
in property values.

overflow

See: *stratified flow*

oversplash

The water that splashes over the top of a sea wall.

ownership of lake bottom land

The ownership (whether public or private) of lake
bottom land is variable according to statutes and court
decisions and the nature of the water body.

Some of the facts about lakes which are considered
relevant by the courts are:

1. Navigability
2. Size

3. Meandered or not meandered
4. History of past use; prescriptive rights may be outstanding.
5. Presence of game fish (natural)
6. Presence of game fish planted by a public agency.
7. Natural or artificial origin of lake
8. Public ownership of riparian lands

oxbow lake

A term applied to a lake occupying the abandoned channel of a looping meander of a river. *Oxbow* is often used as a descriptive term and also is often the specific in the place name applied to lakes, which roughly resemble an oxbow in shape regardless of the geologic origin. The meander type of oxbow is also sometimes called a loop lake.

paleo lake

One that existed in a past geologic period, and has been extinct for a long period of time.
See: *extinct lake*

paludolac

A lake in the nature of a *morass*, or one that has degenerated into a swampy condition with little or no open water remaining. A *paludolac* is a swamp stage in the evolution of a lake from open water to dry land.

pancake ice

Newly formed ice floating in the form of small circular flat pieces with raised rims.

pan lakes

The word "pan", as a designation for a shallow depression containing a lake, pond, or salt flat, has been used (though perhaps not widely) in the arid region of western United States.

Panne (or pan) is a term for a shallow depression containing temporary or permanent pools, in tidal marshes along some sections of the Atlantic Coast.

paradox lakes

Certain basin features in Michigan, representing sites of lakes which have undergone extinction, no longer contain open surface water but still remain in a marsh condition. Locally these may still retain the *lake* name or may be called "dry lakes". Paradoxically they are neither *lake* nor *dry*. Restoration to an open water condition always remains a potentiality.

paralic swamp

A seashore swamp or marsh; a salt water swamp or marsh.

parameters of lakes

Measurements of form aspects including: depth; length; breadth; area; volume; and shoreline development.

Parameter also applies to biologic, chemical, social and economic measurements.

pasture (lake)

Sometimes applied to areas of aquatic vegetation either submerged or emergent which serves as feeding grounds for fish or other aquatic animals.

The shallows of lakes and other standing waters are also used as feeding grounds by moose, deer and bear and in some locations afford wild pasturage for cattle.

paternoster lakes
A term given to a chain of small lakes in glaciated mountain valleys.

pathogenic bacteria
Bacteria which cause disease. Tests for pathogenic bacteria are commonly made by public health agencies for reports on lake pollution.

pay pond
A privately owned pond to which the public is admitted for a charge for swimming, fishing, and other recreational uses.

peat (lake bottom)
In accounts of lakes, bottom deposits are often described as *peat* or *peaty*. The deposits so-called consist mainly of plant matter, but beyond this the term by itself is indefinite in meaning and may be misleading, because often the material is rarely coarse in texture and rarely bears little resemblance in color, or other respects, to the *peat* of commerce, or the moss and sedge peats comprising deposits in bogs, marshes and swamps.

Coarse textured peat is not likely to occur on lake bottoms, except where a rise in lake level has submerged a bordering shoreland of marsh or bog; or on floodings which cover peat land.

pebble beach
A beach composed of well rounded rock fragments of gravel size; smaller than cobbles. According to the Wentworth size classification *pebbles* have a range in diameter from 4 mm to 64 mm.

pebble marl

See: *marl*

pelagic

On an inland lake a term sometimes applied to the deeper bottom zones, 10 to 20 meters or more, characterized by the absence of aquatic vegetation and the presence of ooze or mud deposition.

pelphyte

A term for lake bottom deposits consisting mainly of fine non-fibrous plant remains.

See: *psephyte*

penstock

A closed tube used to conduct water under pressure from a reservoir to the turbine house.

perched lake

A term for a perennial lake which has a surface level lying at a considerably higher elevation than that of other

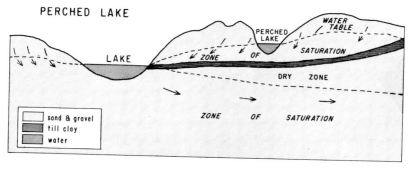

water bodies directly adjacent or closely associated. Such lakes occur in kettles in moraines where they represent the exposure of a local, or "perched" water table; on benches bordering the shores of the Great Lakes; or near the rims of bluffs enclosing a deeply trenched valley.

perennial lake

One that has water in its basin throughout the year and not subject to extreme fluctuations in level.

See: *intermittent lake*

periglacial lakes

Lakes formed during the Pleistocene, on unglaciated land, near the borders of ice sheets.

periphyton

A term for the assemblage of the microorganisms which form a slimy coating on the stems and leaves of submerged plants, stones, and other objects on lake bottoms.

permissive riparian rights

Temporary or limited riparian rights obtained by either verbal or written request, sometimes dependent upon the payment of a fee, for the use or enjoyment of a lake. Permissive rights normally cover short periods of time and may be terminated without prior notice or warning. No prescriptive rights may evolve from permissive use of a lake.

When a person, not a legal riparian, rents a boat and takes it out on a lake he is enjoying a permissive riparian right. This right terminates when the boat is returned.

See: *prescriptive rights*

phantom drain

A drain of unknown origin and location because of no or lost records. Pollution control and health agencies frequently locate the outfalls of drains along lake shores

and stream banks which carry sewage or other objectionable material. In order to regulate promiscuous dumping
of undesirable effluent it is necessary to investigate these
cases and determine what party or parties are involved.
Dye may be introduced at suspected inlets or septic tanks
but this action requires voluntary cooperation and may be
exceedingly slow and possibly unsuccessful. A more drastic
but highly effective procedure would involve plugging
the outlet. Eventually, the guilty party would request an
explanation or file a complaint. Plugging of outlets would
necessarily have to be covered by proper legal authority.

phytoplankton
>   Plant plankton.
>   See: *plankton*

pier
>   A structure which extends from the shore out into the
lake and serves primarily, for the anchorage and landing of
boats. On inland lakes the terms *pier, dock,* and *wharf* are
often applied interchangeably to the same kind of structure. Pier appears occasionally in a place name on the
shoreline of a lake, in the sense of a harbor, haven or
landing.
>   See: *dock*

pierhead line
>   An established line which limits the distance that a
pier, or dock, can be extended from the shore.
>   See: *dock*

pile dwellings (lake)
>   Homes constructed on piles, over lake water, or on
marsh or soft shoreland. Evidence exists that dwellings of

this type were constructed by prehistoric man on lakes in Switzerland and other countries; and the construction of such buildings over lake, stream and marsh has persisted through early historic periods up to the present. Applied to the development of lake land, the pile dwelling has possibilities for the utilization of marsh and soft shore for lake frontage cottage sites, without filling.

piling

Usually wood posts driven into the lake bottom to support docks or other structures. Piling also may be in the form of metal sheets driven in front of banks to protect

Photo — Michigan Department of Conservation
Piling of abandoned boat dock.

them from wave erosion. Submerged posts of old abandoned docks sometimes constitute a menace to boating.

pit lakes (Glacial)

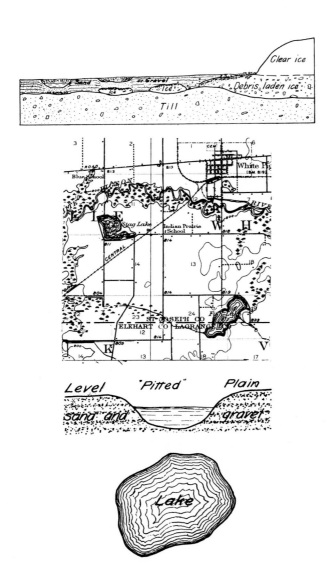

From — Scott, I. D. Inland Lakes of Michigan, Michigan Geological Survey, Publication No. 30, Lansing, Michigan, 1921.

(See definition on next page)

pit lakes (Glacial)

Lakes in basin depressions in glacial outwash plains, which according to theory, resulted from the melting of separate blocks of ice left behind by a retreating glacier and subsequently buried, completely or in part, by glacio-fluvial detritus. The depressions formed by melting of ice blocks may be widely distributed to form pitted plains; or they may consist of a linear succession and a chain of lakes, in a valley filled with outwash.

plankton

A term for an assemblage of micro-organisms, both plant and animal, which float, drift or swim in the water and in their movements are subject to wave and current action. The spelling plancton is sometimes used in older limnologic literature.

See: *seston*

planted fish

Fry or legal sized fish released in a lake to provide for future or immediate fishing.

plash

A shallow piece of standing water; a pool made by inundation or by rain; a puddle. This old English word now appears infrequently and is confined to literary use. If given a technical application, it would supply a term needed to peculiarize those extensive shallow sheets of water, and smaller ponds, lakes or pools which follow heavy rains, rainy seasons, melting snow and river floods, on flatwoods, flats, slashes, marshes, wet prairies and river flood plains. These *plash* waters are transitory and do not have the definite forms, shore lines and other attributes of permanent lakes, but under some conditions may persist for weeks or even months.

platted bottom land

The submerged bottom lands of many non-meandered lakes in Oakland County, Michigan have been divided concurrently with the platting of the upland. Each lot has a portion of the lake bottom included within its boun-

PLATTED BOTTOMLAND

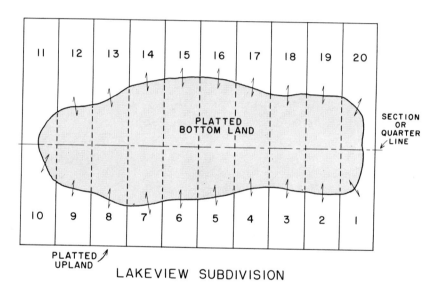

LAKEVIEW SUBDIVISION

daries and the total acreage is recorded on the tax records.

Platting of bottom lands and payment of taxes on bottom lands, would appear to provide these riparian owners with a higher degree of control of lake waters.

platted lot corners (lake)

A lot, adjacent to or near a lake, that has been accurately located by standard surveying techniques. Corners of the lot may be staked but the initial reference points are permanent.

The safest lot survey for a cautious buyer is one that provides two established stakes on the upland. A line connecting these two stakes forms the back of the lot. Sides are established by sighting an angle toward the lake and merely describing its length by stating that it extends to the water line. If a four stake, closed survey, is used in a lake lot description, a drop in water level may leave the lot stranded, with no legal access to the lake.

platting, lake frontage

The technique of dividing a tract of land into individual lots. Many states require that a registered engineer conduct the survey and that proposed plats be reviewed and approved prior to the sale of lots.

The plat itself, or drawing, is accurate as to scale and may include part or all of the following:

1. Dedication clause covering the intent to subdivide by owners.
2. Location, size and description of the tract being platted, including detailed description of monuments.
3. Number, location and dimensions of each lot.
4. Location and dimension of right of ways for sidewalks, alleys, roads, streets, and service easements.
5. Location and dimension of promenades, parks and beaches.
6. Location and dimension of outlots.
7. Dedication clause covering the use of promenades, beaches, parks, roads, alleys and sidewalks by lot owners or the public.
8. Engineer's certificate and certificates of approvals.

There appears to be considerable latitude in platting procedures that are permissible under existing laws.

As crowding and conflicting uses of the lake become more critical, new methods of local control are sought. Some subdividers have reserved a narrow strip of riparian land around the entire lake. Platted lots extend up to this strip but do not extend to the water. Lot owners are granted access conditionally to the lake across the reserved strip. A lot owner for cause can be denied access to the lake. Some projects call for the formation of a lake association, after the sale of a specified percentage of the lots. The rights, title and interest to the riparian strip and lake is transferred to the association which in turn assumes jurisdiction.

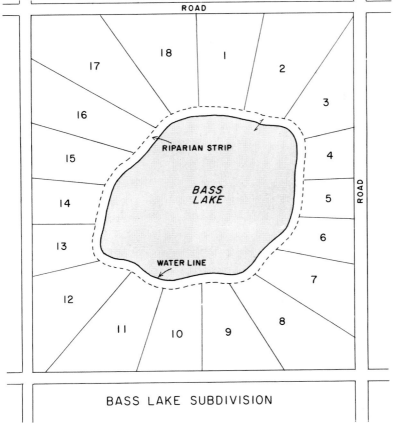

BASS LAKE SUBDIVISION

Serious legal problems arise in respect to the following:
1. Public access to beaches and promenades.
2. Abandonment of platted promenades, beaches, parks, roads, sidewalks and service easements.
3. Public access to the lake over a public road or sidewalk that terminates at the water line.
4. Individual prescriptive rights over platted promenades, beaches, parks, roads, sidewalks and service easements.
5. Legal continuity of connected promenades; can the owners from one subdivision use the promenade of an adjacent subdivision?

Due to intense economic pressure for frontage on high quality lakes, in some cases the original platted lots are divided into small sub-lots to accommodate more cottages.

Many of the above legal problems would not arise if specific language had been used on the plat.

playa

A dry flat-floored basin, usually filled with clayey sediment, which holds water, and becomes a lake temporarily after rains. In usage, the term is generally restricted to the arid regions of the United States.

plerotic water

The term was proposed by O. E. Meinzer in 1939 for the water of the zone of saturation. It is more precise in meaning than *ground water*, and less likely to be misleading.

See: *ground water lake*

pleuston

In the classification of aquatic plants a subdivision of seston, namely: higher plants which float on or in the water.

plunge point

The place where a wave breaks as it approaches the shore, and where the water either plunges over or spills over the crest to form the *uprush* on the foreshore.

plunge pools

Waterfalls have the power to corrade or excavate, holes of considerable size in the rock beds onto which they plunge. When the falls cease to exist, or the rivers are diverted, the basins so created may be occupied by lakes. Lakes in the Grand Coulee in the State of Washington are cited as examples of the *plunge pool* type. The number of occurrences of such lakes in the United States is small and their economic significance is minor.

pluvial lakes

A description for lakes that existed, in the Great Basin of western United States, during the Glacial Epoch and in a period with a colder and more humid climate than the present.

pocket

The application of this word to a water body is very unusual. Only two instances, so far as known have been recorded on maps, namely along the lower course of the Altamaha River in Glynn County, Georgia, and in the Mississippi River bottom lands in Lauderdale County, Tennessee. No information about these features is available other than inferences which can be drawn from the maps on which they are located. The feature in Georgia is known as Old Womans Pocket and appears to be a tumor-like enlargement in a secondary channel of the river. The second water body known as Wardlows Pocket is a small narrow elongate body which is possibly a remnant of water in an old abandoned channel of the Mississippi, or possibly merely in a depression resulting from circumstances of deposition of flood plain sediments. (We are indebted to M. F. Burrill, Office of Geography, U. S. Department of Interior, Washington, D. C. for calling our attention to the above two geographic locations).

pocket beach
A beach at the head of a bay.
See: *bayhead beach*

pocoson
See: *bays (ponds)*

point (pointe)
A peninsula or piece of land, with a sharp or tapering end, projecting from the shore into the lake. In usage, *point* (or French-Canadian word *pointe*) may apply either to high land, or to low land, the latter often barely above water level. Often the feature so named has no "point" but is rounded and more in the nature of a head or cape.

In Michigan, usage is not uniformly consistent, but generally "point" includes all or the greater part of the projection of land, rather than only its tapered end.

pollution (of lakes)
The term *pollution* is relative in meaning and subject to various interpretations, because of the multiple uses that lakes are subject to, and the great range in attitude of people concerned with it and affected by it. A pollutant may be present in amounts or kinds that are highly objectionable, and not be sufficient to constitute *pollution* according to standard tests accepted by the public health officials. Pollution may be concentrated in one part of a lake and not affect the whole body of water. Introduction

of a sewage effluent into a lake may be harmful, or from another point of view it could be beneficial because it results in an increase in aquatic plant production. A toxic chemical introduced into the water might destroy some forms of aquatic life and affect the value of the water for some industrial use or as a source of drinking water, but have no adverse effect on use for boating.

Pollution is the addition to the water or shores of a lake, of any material which endangers human health, or destroys or adversely affects aquatic life, recreational and other values. Commonly the word pollution implies the presence of pathogens. Conservationists however, use the term with more latitude. In addition to untreated sewage and other organic wastes which are ordinarily pathogenic, chemicals, factory and mine wastes, erosion sediments in suspension and on the bottom, used water and other materials objectionable but not ordinarily pathogenic, may be regarded as pollutants. Pollution may come from the runoff from agricultural lands which have been heavily fertilized and treated with pesticides. Generally no clear distinction is observed between *pollution* and *contamination* either in scientific literature or in common speech.

Technically a lake is *polluted* only when the deleterious substances added are in excess of its ability to assimilate them. Pollution ordinarily results from human activities, but also may result from natural causes.

A precise expression of pollution may be based on laboratory tests, as for example when *"pollution"* is determined on the basis of amount of dissolved oxygen in the water, an amount 5 ppm or lower; or on the basis of a *bioassay*. Both the qualitative, or loosely inclusive meaning of pollution, and the precise laboratory expression may be found wanting and unsatisfactory under some particular set of circumstances.

That which is harmful or injurious to one riparian or user of the water may not be to another with quite different interests.

See: *smirchment*

pollution indicator organism

Certain plant and animal forms thrive in polluted water. With proper knowledge and experience, the presence of these forms may be accepted as indicators of pollution. The rat-tailed maggot is frequently present in vast numbers in the bottom of lakes subject to the discharge of raw sewage. A prolific growth of blue-green filamentous algae will also occur as a result of pollution by sewage.

polynya

A word of Russian origin. It has been used as a term for areas of open sea water in Arctic pack ice, and other open water bodies on Polar ice, but also according to the Navigation Dictionary (published 1956 by the U. S. Hydrographic Office Bull. 220), a *pool* and a *glade* may be called a *polynya*.

pond

The term *pond* is generally applied to small impoundments for a source of water for livestock and for other uses on farms. *Pond* is also applied to bodies of water created for feeding and nesting grounds for waterfowl; and for pools of water designed for hatching and containing fish. The term *millpond* is in use for small impoundments created for generating power for grist mills and saw mills. However, without consistency, the term *pond* is applied to large impoundments and used interchangeably with *lake, reservoir flooding, floodwater* and *basin.* Pond is also a common term for natural water bodies and according to prevailing usage it implies that the body so called is small and inferior. However, in some geographic sections of the United States and in numerous isolated local instances, pond and lake have been used interchangeably and applied in the naming of water bodies, without distinction in meaning. In exceptional instances *pond* has been applied in place names to practically all of the various kinds of water bodies often seemingly capriciously, for example, even to coastal *estuaries, sounds* and *bays.* In the physiographic evolution of a water body from open water to dry land, *pond* represents a transition stage in filling with vegetation, between open water and marsh.

pond scum

A scum of filamentous algae typically green, sometimes brownish, which exists as floating mats and nets (flots) on the surface of lakes and ponds. On stagnant ponds, it may form a nearly complete cover. Unsightly and obnoxious to humans but not so regarded by frogs.

pondweeds

A popular name applied mostly to species of *Potamogeton* and *Najas.* These are submerged aquatics, some with floating leaves. They are often the principal components of "weed beds" in lakes, and supply a habitat for organisms which in turn supply food for fish and wildfowl.

pontoon boat

The basic design principle of a *pontoon boat* is a platform supported by two parallel metal pontoons. Both ends of the pontoons are shaped to facilitate movement over the water surface. Locomotion is normally provided by outboard motors.

Most pontoon boats have a railing around the platform and some have a canopy. More elaborate models have permanent cabins resplendent with all the facilities of a cabin cruiser. One company specializes in the manufacture of an adaptor kit for house trailers. After removing the axel and wheels, the trailer can be firmly attached to the deck structure for use on lakes and streams.

pool

The term *pool* has been used: for the deeper holes in rivers and in shallow lakes; for small stagnant bodies of water in a marsh or swamp; as an alternate term for *pond* at fish hatcheries; and also for small transient bodies of water accumulated in depressions following rains.

Pool is sometimes applied to both small and large bodies of impounded waters. As an example in Michigan, the separate impoundments, or floodings, some as large as 800 acres in the Seney Wild Life Refuge in Schoolcraft County have been designated *pools* by the Federal Agency in charge of the Refuge.

Among the several applications of this term to bodies of water, it has been applied to small impoundments back of low dams across trout streams. "Dams . . . have been widely used to make *pools* suitable for large trout." (Hubbs, Carl L. and others, *Methods for the improvement of Trout Streams*, Bulletin No. 1., Institute of Fisheries Research, Ann Arbor, Michigan, p. 22.)

In the terminology of the hydraulic engineer the level of the water in a reservoir, or impoundment back of a dam, is the "pool-line" regardless of the size of the reservoir.

See: *beach pool*
plunge pool

pool line

The level of water in a reservoir indicating the amount in storage for power (and sometimes also recreational) purposes is the "pool line" or "pool level".

portage

In travel by water, a recognized connecting land route between lakes and streams over which boats are carried or otherwise transported.

Modern portage technique between two lakes.

A marine railway type of portage for large boats and cabin cruisers utilizes a narrow gage railway. The boat to be portaged is positioned over an adjustable cradle mounted on railroad wheels which rides on a section of underwater track. After the boat is secured to the cradle, a cable winch pulls it out of the water and over the portage to the launching point. Passengers and luggage may stay aboard during this type of portage.

portage lake
In the early days where travel was largely on waterways and by canoes and boats, a lake which served as a connecting link between two rivers, or two larger lakes, was called a *portage lake*. A number of lakes in Michigan and other states which have the present day place name Portage originally served this purpose.

potable water
Water suitable for drinking purposes. Detailed laboratory tests by competent public health agencies are necessary to determine the safety of drinking water. Generally, untreated lake water is not potable water, but in wilderness areas lake water is easily rendered potable by use of chlorination kits.

potash lakes
A term applied to closed and enclosed lakes, in semi-arid and arid regions, whose brine contain a high proportion of salts of potassium. In the United States such lakes occur in the western part of the Sand Hills region of Nebraska.

pothole (lake, pond)
The term pothole is in current use in Michigan for small pit depressions, generally circular or elliptical, and a few feet to 40 or 50 feet deep. They are constructional in origin and most common in outwash plains and recessional moraines but are also recognized in till plains. Many have dry bottoms, but many also contain lakes, intermittent ponds, and bogs of various kinds.

The term *pothole* has been used by wildlife specialists for shallow depressions in the prairies of Minnesota and the Dakotas. These contain intermittent ponds, or marshes and though of small size, mostly 10 acres or less, are important nesting places for waterfowl.

In some coastal marshes *pothole* has been applied to small circular steep-sided pits locally known as "rotten spots" which contain water at or below low tide level; and also to small shallow hollows in the flat limestone terrain east and south of the Everglades in Florida.

Pothole also has a geologic connotation namely a small circular or elliptical hole in the rock bed of a river scoured out by current action. Potholes of this type have no considerable significance as basins for ponds or lakes.

pound

An old word for an artificially banked body of water. Originally *pound* and *pond* were identical; *pond* was a variant.

power pond

A term sometimes given to an impoundment or reservoir created primarily for the generation of electric power.

p.p.b.

Abbreviation for parts per billion in terms of units of weight. Used to report the presence of materials in extremely minute quantities which may be important as environmental factors for fish or in relation to public health and industrial use of water.

Increasing utilization of insecticides and herbicides has resulted in *pollution* or *smirchment* at a concentration previously considered unimportant but unfortunately some of these materials are extremely toxic in low concentration and others may be progressively accumulated and stored in plant or animal tissue from water containing trace amounts.

p.p.m.

Abbreviation for parts per million in terms of units of weight. Used to report the availability or presence of salts, nutrients, gases and toxic materials in water.

prescriptive rights (pertaining to lakes)

Prescriptive rights are rights that mature as a result of long, open, continuous, and notorious (trespass) use. Under common law, prescriptive rights to surface water are complex and usually have to be submitted to a court for interpretation.

presque isle

Nearly, or almost an island. In its application to inland lakes, the term *presque isle* is defined as a promontory, or peninsula, with its head or end section separated from the shore by a sag, or low gap, only slightly above water level. Or the upland may be tied to the mainland by a strip of lake bottom, not necessarily a bar, exposed as a land surface by a drop in lake level.

primitive lakes

Primitive is sometimes applied to lakes located in primitive regions or in wilderness. The shoreline and water of a primitive lake are essentially unmodified by human activities; or remain in a pristine condition.

See: *wilderness lakes*

private lake

One owned by an individual, group of individuals or by a club with restricted membership, in contrast to one to which the public has legal access. *Private* as applied to a lake may be a matter for court determination, and hinge, in addition to riparian ownership, upon such factors as: origin of the water; size of the water body; use of the water; influents and effluents and their navigability; and whether or not the fish in the lake have been planted at public expense.

productivity, of a lake

The amount of organisms grown; expressed with reference to total, kinds, time and rate.

profundal

See: *basin* for illustration
beach profile for illustration
See: *profundal bottoms*

profundal bottoms

The deeper bottoms of a lake in contrast to *shallows*, *shoals* and littoral shelves. Also a limnological concept, the *profundal* is a life zone lying at greater depths than the *littoral* and *sublittoral*. Emergent and submerged plants of the littoral are absent, and the communities of flora and fauna are those adapted to a low content of oxygen, or oxygen-less conditions.

See: *littoral*
sublittoral

proglacial lakes

Ponded waters formed at the front of receding ice sheets with ice walls forming a part of the shoreline of the lake. Such lakes were formed in Michigan and other states during the Pleistocene, and their locations are known by the location of lacustrine sediments. Small lakes remain in some of the old glacial lake bed plains, but it is not certain that they are relics of the original glacial lakes.

promenade

A right of way (improved or unimproved) along the shoreline dedicated for walking. Many lake development schemes incorporated promenades along the beach or boardwalk promenades built out over the water surface for use by the owners of lake subdivision lots. The promenade may extend around the entire lake or be restricted to the shoreline in front of one subdivision.

promontory

A headland; generally regarded as a prominent highland feature, whereas *peninsula* and *point* may be either high land or low land.

psammolittoral

A term for the sandy shore zone, including both the dry and submerged parts.

psammon

A limnological term for the environment composed of the sandy beach and the sand bottom lakeward from the water line.

psephyte

A term for lake bottom deposits consisting largely of coarse fibrous remains of plants. More precise and therefore preferable to peat as a term for this kind of bottom.

public access (to a lake)

An approach over land that is publicly owned or over land subject to prescriptive rights vested in the public, over which the public may gain access to a lake. The term access, as commonly accepted, also implies the right of egress inasmuch as one must also leave a lake after having gained access.

Photo — Michigan Conservation Department

Limited parking facilities may effectively limit the overcrowding of public beaches.

The access may be improved with parking and other conveniences on the shore; or may be without any improvements, or even a roadway.

Opposition to public access may arise because it may result in overcrowding, noise and litter and thus lowers the value of the private riparian land.

public access plats

Private non-riparian land fronting on or located near public access tracts. On high quality inland lakes such backland may command as high a price as riparian land. Owners may enjoy the benefits of lake use without bearing the expense of management or having to tolerate the problems of crowding and conflicting uses common to lakeshores.

Within certain limits property values on some lakes actually increase proportionally to the distance from the lakeshore. This peculiar phenomenon of real estate values reflects faulty planning in the original development of frontage land and failure to correct the problem arising therefrom.

public bottom land

A term used in Michigan for certain tracts of land covered by the water of impoundments and artificial lakes that have reverted to the State for non-payment of taxes.

public fish

Fish planted in a lake, either by a public agency, or by public employees, or at public expense with prior approval of private owners involved. The migration of public fish from a public lake to a private lake need not change the legal classification of the private lake. Progeny of the original planted public fish could under certain circumstances be assumed to be of mixed heritage and the chain of ownership might need interpretation by a court.

public fishing site

See: *launching area*

public highway (water)

In Michigan P. A. 1899, Act 175 public highways were surveyed through the St. Clair Flats for perpetual public use. These water highways were intended to serve for access to the "underwater lots" leased by the state for development as cottage sites; filling above water level would be required for development of the lots.

See: *underwater lot*
waterway

public lake

One to which the public has legal access, and the right to use either the water only, or both the water and the shore, for one or more purposes, such as navigation, fishing and hunting.

If the public obtained access to the lake by use of a public fishing access point, the people so entering would be limited to making reasonable use of the open water. Intensive use of shallow water in front of private cottages and use of private beaches could possibly be challenged as being unreasonable or a violation of privacy.

See: *private lake*

public shooting grounds

Under Michigan law, submerged and swamp lands belonging to the state of Michigan may be dedicated as public shooting grounds. The taking of wildfowl is permitted under special state regulations.

public water

Water that is navigable by Federal test or Court decree, that is legally accessible over public lands or water impressed with prescriptive rights vested in the public.

puddin' bed

A localism for an exposed lake bed which consists of a very soft, pulpy, watery mass of plant remains. The term refers to the very recently exposed lake bottoms which generally border the open water of the lake, and are too mushy to support the weight of a man, or even smaller animal such as a dog. The *puddin' bed* thus differs from the surface of "quaking" bogs composed of firmly matted marsh or bog vegetation and therefore capable of supporting a considerable weight.

puddle

A small closed pool, especially dirty water; an ephemeral pool left by a rain; a *plash*. Often applied in a derogatory sense to a *lake* or *pond*. As a verb puddle means to render impervious. In the construction of artificial ponds, often clayey bottoms are *puddled* by engineering measures; also in instances natural depressions holding water have had their bottoms puddled by the trampling and wallowing of animals that made use of them as water holes.

pull-over

A simple pole structure built over short portages to facilitate transporting canoes and boats. A canoe is skidded over the pull-over, in an upright position with much of the duffle and equipment aboard.

Loaded canoe being portaged over a pull-over.

pulpy peat

This term is often applied to the grayish, greenish or brownish, soft, mushy, fine textured mass, mainly plant matter accumulated on lake bottoms. Such material is also sometimes called macerated peat and sedimentary peat.

See: *ävja-gyttja*
gyttja
peat

pumped storage reservoir

Many hydro-electric plants have uneven hourly demands for electricity. Under ideal conditions, excess power may be used to lift downstream water into small temporary pumped storage reservoirs. This water then becomes available to produce electricity during the "peak" demand hours. This type of storage reservoir has little multiple use value due to the extreme diurnal variations in water level.

Punkhole

A rare hydronym. It appears as a place name in one location in Herkimer County, New York. (See: Piseco Lake Topographic Quadrangle U. S. Geol. Survey). Here it is a small marsh traversed by a small stream, but originally was a fluvial pond, or lake, a hole or widening in the channel of the marsh stream. (This feature was called to the attention of the authors by M. F. Burrill, Office of Geography, U. S. Department of Interior.)

purgatorial reliction (inland lakes)

A proposed term for lake bed that has been recently exposed by recession of a shoreline and whose natural fate is uncertain, that is whether it is destined to remain *land* — or revert to a water surface. Instances may occur where the recession is more prolonged than that produced by the normal fluctuations in lake levels; the riparian owner may assume that the recession is permanent (or may be opportunistic) and proceed with structures or "improvements" on the exposed lake bed. Subsequently, however, former high lake levels may return and produce distressing complications. In Michigan the riparian owner can exercise an *exclusive* easement over the use of this land, but he cannot legally modify it in any way that would interfere with the eventual return of the water.

See: *reliction*

movable freehold

Recession of the waterline, temporary or permanent?

purpresture (pourpresture)

Private encroachment on, or appropriation of lands and waters which are common or public. A structure, or fill, built on the bed of a lake below high water mark; or a structure such as a dock which is a permanent obstruction to navigation may be declared a *purpresture* in court decisions.

put and take system of fish management

A shop term descriptive of the process of planting legal size fish each year, prior to the fishing season for the benefit of those fishing in the lake. The fact that these fish may survive for succeeding years is of secondary importance.

putrescible waste
Matter, usually of animal origin, that is subject to the process of putrefaction. The resulting odors may be most oppressive.

pyric ponds
Ponds, or pools, in shallow holes and sinks due to uneven burning and subsidence resulting from fires in peat deposits, and to those in sinks due to underground fires which consume lignite and coal beds.

pythmic
Of or pertaining to lake bottoms. (For origin of term see Klugh, 1923, *Ecology,* Volume 4, page 372.)

quaking bog
See: *bog*
flotant

quarry ponds
A quarry is an open surface working, or excavation, made for the extraction of stone, from bedrock, for industrial and other uses. Often the excavations are deep and when abandoned fill up with water to make lakes or ponds, which may have considerable economic value. Inasmuch as the basins are cut out of bedrock and the walls are usually nearly vertical, quarry ponds are distinct from those of abandoned gravel pits, clay pits, borrow pits and others belonging in this category of artificial water bodies.
See: *artificial lakes*
ponds

quondam island (in lake basin)

See: *environment* for illustration

Formerly an island. An island originally set in a lake, but now set in a marsh, bog, or other kind of low land which represents the site of a former water body. In some locations the original lake level may be restored temporarily at intervals, and thus make the *quondam island* for the time being a true island.

quondam outlets

The term *quondam* is proposed for abandoned outlets, those which no longer contain an active or even intermittent stream. An abandoned channel or a linear marsh or swamp leading out of the lake may still exist, or proof that an outflowing stream once existed may be obtained from early maps or other historical accounts.

race

An artificial channel, or canal leading from a dam to a water wheel, or other contrivance for generating power. The stream leaving the dam is the *head race;* and that leaving the wheel is the *tail race.*

raft lakes

Bodies of river water impounded by natural obstructions of logs or driftwood. Trees dislodged from river banks during floods carried downstream may meet with some obstruction and accumulate until they form a huge jam or "raft" sufficient to act as a dam and back up the water. The most commonly cited examples of raft lakes are those of the Red River in Louisiana. Such lakes are relatively short-lived.

See: *floodwood*

raised beach

An old beach lying at an elevation above the present beach. The "raised" position does not represent an uplift of the land surface; it is more probable that the bench or terrace represents a former high stage of the lake.

ramp

See: *boat ramp*

rat-tailed maggot

A fly maggot which is often found in foul, septic lakes and ponds. It is provided with a long air tube (the tail) which it extends above the surface of the water.

See: *pollution indicator organism*

reach (in a lake)

A relatively long straight stretch of water as along a shore line; also a narrow arm or indentation *reaching* into the land. The term also may be applied to a straight stretch of shore or to a narrow extension of land into a lake.

reasonable use (lake waters)

No absolute rule has been laid down by courts as to what constitutes "reasonable" or "unreasonable" use of lake and stream waters. Court decisions have varied and are likely to continue to vary according to the questions involved, the time and circumstances of individual cases. In theory, a "reasonable" use is one that does not impair the rights of other riparians, or conflict with public rights.

recession (lake)

Change in the position of the waterline, or shoreline, from its original position to a lower position with a corresponding exposure of the lake bottom. Recession may represent a single gradual decrease in lake level; or may

Impairment of the recreational value of a lake by drop in lake level and recession of the waterline.

represent successive low stages; and may be temporary, or may be permanent. A recession may result in loss in value of frontage property and be harmful in other respects, or on the other hand, may be beneficial depending upon local circumstances.

See: *extinction*

stage

recession flats (lake basins)
Flat bottoms of lakes exposed by recession of shore-lines or drop in lake levels.

See: *mudflats*

Wide recession flat.

recharge lagoon
See: *ground water recharge pond*

recreational pool
Residual storage over and above the required capacity of a flood control reservoir. The designed capacity of the flood control structure can be increased to provide for a permanent recreational pool without impairing its emergency flood capacity. Also called a conservation pool.

recreational slum (lake)

This term has begun to make its appearance in discussions, meetings and papers. It is used to describe lakeshore development composed of small, cheap and shoddy cottages on narrow lots.

red lakes

Reddish water in lakes may be due to: (1) iron secreting bacteria and planktonic organisms which have reddish color; (2) ferrous iron compound in solution; (3) reddish clay or inorganic colloidal matter held in suspension; (4) the organic matter from bogs sometimes imparts a reddish brown color.

redd

A spawning bed (or nest) of gravel, constructed in shallow, cool, clear water by trout.

reeds (lake)

The reeds common in the shallow water of nearly extinct lakes and ponds and in watery marshes are: Tall Reed Grass, *(Phragmites sp.)* and Bur Reed, *(Sparganium spp.)*

reef

A shoal consisting of a ridge of sand, gravel or hard rock. Reefs are recognized and mapped on the Lake Survey Charts for the Great Lakes; the term appears rarely in descriptions of inland lakes.

reflection basin (reflection pool)

A shallow basin or pool constructed for the beautification of landscaped grounds. The shape and location of the basin is designed to harmonize with the landscape and architectural features and may also be successfully used to enhance the beauty of a particular feature. Fine exam-

Photo — Michigan Tourist Council

Reflection basin at General Motors Technical Center, Michigan.

ples of reflection basins are those found on the Capitol grounds in Washington, D. C. and those associated with the Taj Mahal in India.

regular shoreline

Straight or smooth broadly curved and not broken by projections, indentations, or deep embayments. The smooth shore may have been inherited from the original form of the basin, or may have been developed by erosional and

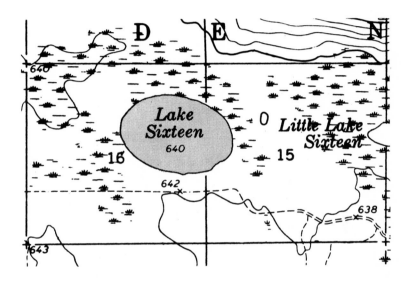

Lake with a regular shoreline, Delta County, Michigan.

depositional processes in the evolution of the lake. Some closed lakes in pot holes, or kettles, in glaciated regions; some lime sink lakes; some crater lakes, and some isolated and remnental lakes set in marshes are remarkable for their unbroken margins and rounded forms.

See: *irregular* shoreline

rejuvenated lake

An old, dying or near extinct lake that has had its bottom deposits, or filling of vegetation removed from its basin by dredging, and thereby restored to its original depths.

The words *rejuvenated* and *restored* are often used interchangeably. The engineering operations to which they refer may result in neither (if the words are to be construed literally) but merely in improvement, or an environmental change.

reliction (lake land)

The exposure of lake bottom by natural recession of the shoreline or drop in water level, thereby making former water surface *land*. The exposed area is subject to riparian ownership and use as land. The recession necessarily must be relatively permanent; that resulting from seasonal fluctuations in lake levels, and even short cycles of low water, followed by return of normal levels is so temporary that it may be ignored as reliction. Recessions of shorelines have taken place in the past, but these old events, preceding man's occupation of the land and riparian ownership, are not involved per se in the concept of reliction.

See: *bottom land, lake*
purgatorial reliction

repi (from the Greek for sink or subsidence)

This word is useful as a group term for all lakes, ponds, or other standing water bodies related to sinks, or to subsidence, of land surface.

See: *suffosion lakes*

reservoir

The term reservoir is commonly applied to waters held in storage in either artificial or natural basins and impoundments primarily for a source of water for power, municipal, industrial, domestic or flood control uses. In usage the term is not consistently distinguished from other hydronyms. *Reservoir, Basin, Storage Basin, Lake, Pond,. Impoundment and Flowage,* all have been applied according to circumstances and location, to the same kind of water body. A reservoir is usually a surface water body, artificial in that it is an impoundment of a stream, or occupies a man-made basin, but the water body of a natural basin, such as a lake, may also be a *reservoir.* In some locations, the reservoir capacity is materially increased by bank (ground water) storage.

resort lake

A *resort lake* is one which has private cottages on its shores or provided with hotels or camps where people may go for entertainment and recreation. This is in con-

Photo — Michigan Tourist Council

Lake resort.

trast to one which has no shore development, although it may be frequented occasionally for fishing and hunting.

A *lake resort* may be a single hotel or other establishment, located on or near a lake shore, and maintained primarily for guests, seeking recreation or amusement. *Resort* may be applied to a community, village, or town where the principal business is catering to visitors seeking recreation.

restored lake

One that has been changed from a condition of very low water level, or "dry" bottom, to its original high water level. This may have been accomplished by engineering measures; or the restoration may have been a natural process.

See: *rejuvenated lake*

retarding basin

A flood water control device. A storage basin back of a dam with a permanent opening. This is in contrast to a storage basin back of a dam provided with gates.

reversed inlet

In instances where a lake lies in a river flood plain, or in flat terrain, and is subject to flooding and very high levels, a stream which is normally an influent to the lake may have its flow temporarily reversed. In other instances where a lake level has been raised by a dam on its outlet, or in some cases by a beaver dam, a stream which formerly flowed into the lake may have its flow reversed and become an outlet.

reversed outlet

See: *outlet*

revetment

A facing of stone, concrete or other material to protect the banks of a lake from wave erosion.

rhohelos

In the terminology of Ecology, a non-alluvial marsh traversed by a stream. The term is fitting for a large proportion of wet marsh, which represents former lake areas now filled with peat. The streams traversing the marshes are nearly bankless and carry very little inorganic sediment.

ria lakes

Those formed at the mouths of rivers, where the valleys have been submerged or "drowned".

Photo – Michigan Conservation Department

Ria lake on shore of Lake Michigan.

rich lakes

A term applied to those "rich" in nutrients in the waters and bottom soils, and capable of supporting an abundant flora and fauna.

See: *eutrophic lakes*

rift lakes

Lakes occupying narrow troughs or valleys that have resulted from graben faulting. Also called *graben lakes.*

ripa

A legal term for the bank of a stream or a lake.

riparian

The term riparian may be used as a noun, and means a person with rights to water by virtue of ownership of land bordering the bank of a stream or waterline of a lake. The term is more commonly used as an adjective, as in *riparian rights* or *riparian doctrine.*

riparian land

See: *riparian rights*

riparian reservation, lake

A clause, usually included in a deed, reserving unto the vendor all or part of the riparian rights to a lake. One party may sell a riparian lot to another party but reserve all hunting or fishing rights for his private use. The legality of a riparian reservation would be questionable unless the original owner of a lake, having no inlet or outlet, was the sole owner of all riparian lands fronting upon the lake; and therefore owned all rights, title and interest to the lake.

Riparian reservations are most common in the sale of lots fronting upon reservoirs, artificial lakes and ponds.

riparian rights (lake)

The rights a person, or group in common, has by virtue of ownership of land, abutting the banks or fronting on the water of a lake. The riparian in theory and by common law has certain rights and privileges in the use of water which the non-riparian does not have. However, the "rights" are limited and are constantly being subjected to question. Interpretation of "reasonable" or "unreasonable" use and degree of ownership permissible for water, ice, aquatic vegetation and lake bottom; and conflicts between individual interests and controls and regulations in the public interest are matters for court decisions in specific cases.

The riparian also enjoys certain exclusive rights to the use of his beach, the shallow water adjacent to his land, the ice immediately in front of his property, and the bottom land immediately in front of his property. These rights may be defended against invasion by other riparians.

riparian vegetation (lake)

Hydrophytic vegetation growing in the immediate vicinity of a lake, close enough so that its annual *evapotranspiration* represents a factor in the *lake regimen*.

> See: *evaporation*
> *transpiration*
> *lake regimen*

ripple

A very small wave: one whose period is arbitrarily defined as three seconds or less.

ripple marks

Fairly regular micro-ridges produced on near-shore bottoms by current or wave action; and on land by wind action.

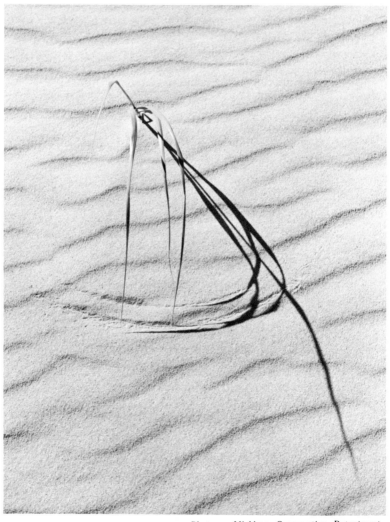

Photo — Michigan Conservation Department

Ripple marks.

Ripple marks on shallow sandy bottoms and on wet beaches of a lake excite popular interest, and, though transient, may in some locations be regarded as an aesthetic feature.

riprap

Coarse stones, natural boulders and cobbles or artificially broken rock fragments laid (either loosely or cemented) against the basal slope of a bank for the purpose of preventing wave cutting.

See: *sea wall*

riverine lakes

An inclusive term for impoundments created by dams across rivers. *Riverine* includes impounded water bodies variously called: *reservoirs; ponds; basins; storage basins; flowages; floodings; and floodwaters.*

rock

A projection, above its water surface, of hard rock in the nature of a small island or islet. *Rocks* are recognized

A rock, Rainy Lake, Ontario, Canada.

and given place names in the Great Lakes, but instances of recognition, by place names, in inland lakes are infrequent. This kind of lake feature is commonly considered a menace to navigation. Any economic values are generally minor but their aesthetic values may be of major significance in some localities.

rock lakes

Lakes that occupy basins enclosed by bedrock. Where "rock" is used to designate a class, or when it is the specific in the place name for a lake, it usually implies that the lake margin is bordered by rock cliffs, or that the shore zone is strewn with bedrock fragments.

rollways

During the early days of lumbering in the Lake States, as a part of the operations, logs harvested from the forest were transported to nearby streams or lakes and rolled over banks, or bluffs, into the water, hence to be floated, or rafted, to saw mills. The high banks so used were called *rollways*. Relics of the old rollways and their effects on stream and lake bottoms, still remain.

Rollway is also a term for the over-flow portion of a dam.

ropey sand

A special term applied to non-wetting sand that retains a rope like shape when introduced through a tube into a container of water.

See: *non-wetting sand*

rough fish

Those species such as carp and sucker, considered undesirable, predatory or obnoxious by anglers. Regulations and licensing pertaining to the taking of rough fish vary by states.

rubble beach

One composed of angular rock fragments less than boulder size. Rubble is similar to *shingle* except that fragments are blocky or chunky rather than flattish, but often no sharp distinction between the two is made in descriptions.

run of the river reservoir

One made by a low dam. The water body back of the dam is narrow and pretty well held to the width of the river channel. Such reservoirs are usually made for the purpose of aiding navigation, and are not subject to wide changes in level.

See: *storage reservoir*

rush lakes

The most conspicuous rushes associated with lakes are species of *Scirpus,* commonly called bulrush. The abundance of bulrush in the shallow waters is the source of the specific name *Rush.* Other rushes associated with shallow shoreline water and wet lowland are species of spike rush (*Eleocharis)* and species of *Juncus.*

sac

This word, of French origin, appears as a term for a water feature near Grand Haven, Michigan (Muskegon Quadrangle, Topographic Sheet, U. S. Geological Survey). Here, the place name "The Sac" is given to a stomach-like inland extension, or bay, of the wide channel of Grand River.

sag ponds

Small ponds or lakes which occur in basins due to subsidence along fault lines. Local in California.

In various parts of the United States "sag" is a common, or folk word for shallow depressions between swells and ridges in undulating terrains, and often the "sags" contain temporary ponds and sometimes permanent water bodies.

salina

A term usually applied to salt encrusted playa flats in arid regions of the United States but also sometimes applied to any lake or pond of salt water.

salinity (of lake water)

Salinity commonly signifies water containing a high concentration of salt or sodium chloride. Technically the term is not so restricted and may refer to water containing chlorides, sulphates and carbonates of sodium, potassium, calcium and magnesium or to total dissolved solids.

Salinity can be expressed also in terms of the chloride content or chlorinity. The formula is:

Salinity 0/00 = 0.030 + 1.8050 x chlorinity 0/00.

The salinity of certain lakes in arid regions greatly exceeds that of the oceans.

salt flat

Salt-encrusted bottom of a dessicated lake.

salt lakes

The term is commonly applied to those whose waters contain a high concentration of sodium chloride ($NaCl$).

salt ponds

A localism for both small and large bodies of salt water in marshes and swamps along the sea coast. The term is also applied to artificial ponds used for evaporation, in the production of salt from sea water.

salvage rights (on inland lakes)

The ownership of lost or abandoned boating and recreation equipment on inland lakes is not clear.

Doubts exist regarding the applicability of maritime law to salvage rights on inland lakes. The uncertainty stems from the fact that the bottom lands of inland lakes in some states represent private property, therefore the maritime law which covers Federal and International waters may not apply.

Insurance policies available to boat owners usually contain language permitting interpretation under: (1) Federal maritime law; (2) State laws; and (3) combination of Federal and State jurisdiction.

sanctuary lake
One located within the bounds of a wildlife sanctuary; or one in which all or some particular species of animals frequenting or living in its waters are protected from molestation by man.

Photo – Michigan Conservation Department

A sanctuary lake at the Michigan State University Biological Station, Wintergreen Lake, Kalamazoo County, Michigan.

sand blanket
Sand spread over a plastic film or other suitable material to improve the recreational value of unsuitable lakeshore. Permits to install sand blankets on clay, stone and weedy lakeshore in Wisconsin require that a maximum of four inches of sand be used and limit the treatment to a depth of three feet.
See: *artificial beach*

sapropel

The product of the decomposition of organically rich lake bottom sediments. The decomposition takes place under *anaerobic* conditions, and the deposit may have a fetid odor from hydrogen sulfide.

satellite lakes

One or more small lakes disconnected and separated from but associated with a single large lake in a single basin. The individual lake represents a separate remnant resulting from a drop in level, or partial extinction of an original single body of water, and is usually set in a marsh or swamp.

savanna(h)

A term used locally for some of the wetland features, in the nature of marsh and wet prairie, along the Atlantic Coast from North Carolina to Florida. They may contain clumps or scattered trees such as the cabbage palmetto, and some are called "pine savannahs".

sawdust shoal

In lumbering in Michigan, and other states saw mills were frequently located on the shores of inland lakes. Sawdust resulting from lumber manufacture was sometimes disposed of directly into the lake. Often wind and current activity transported the sawdust, while still buoyant, and after becoming water-logged sometimes it was deposited in shallow water or on shallow bottom. Old mill refuse remains on lake shores and bottoms for many years and often detracts from scenic values and interferes with boat traffic, beach use and fish production.

scour (glacial lakes)

Lakes occupying depressions, or basins, made by the gouging and abrading action of glaciers passing over soft rocks or moving in pre-existing valleys. In Michigan some of the lakes on Isle Royale, Lake Superior, may occupy basins of this origin.

scuba diving

Sustained diving and underwater swimming accomplished with the aid of compressed air tanks attached to the diver and other specialized equipment.

Photo – Michigan Department of Conservation

Scuba diving.

Normally a summer sport, scuba diving with insulated suits is also becoming known as a winter sport.

The aqualung known as scuba (selfcontained underwater breathing apparatus) was invented in 1942 by the Frenchman, Jacques Ives-Cousteau. The apparatus is widely used for sustained diving and scientific survey of lake bottoms and shallow sea bottoms to depths of 150 feet. Diving is mainly a sport, but is also conducted for scientific purposes and for the recovery of treasures and artifacts.

sea

In place names and other usage *sea* and *lake* are not consistently distinguished. In one place a large body of salt water may be called a *lake,* in another a *sea.* The Great Lakes, Lake Superior and others, are fresh water but by legal definition are *seas.*

Sea may be used as part of a binomial expression describing the water motion in relation to boating on inland lakes as well as on the high seas.

sea cave

A cavity formed in the face of a cliff by wave erosion. Caves formed during past stages of a lake may exist either above or below present lake levels.

sea cliffs

Ordinarily the reference is to cliffs on the coast line of the ocean. However the high bluffs on the shores of the Great Lakes were called "sea cliffs" by G. K. Gilbert (Topographic features of Lake Shores, 5th Annual Report, U. S. Geol. Survey, 1885, pages 69-123).

sea wall

An engineering term for a wall built, on the shore of a lake, of concrete, stone or other material to protect lake shore cottages and other property from damage by storm waves, ice shove, and high water stages. This wall is built even with, or above, the shoreland level to be protected.

Sea wall on a large inland lake.

seadrome (lake)

That portion of a lakeshore that has been developed for servicing float or amphibian aircraft. Normally the facilities provided would include a ramp, hardstand, hangars, fueling equipment and a light repair shop. Off-shore anchorage buoys may be available and the landing area may also be marked with buoys.

.

sealed basin

See: *basin seal*

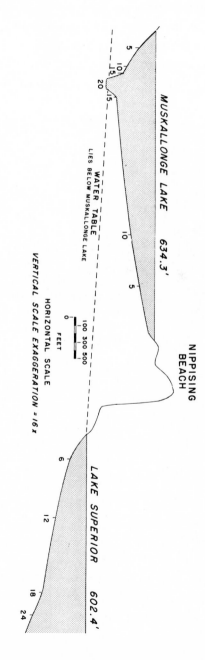

MUSKALLONGE LAKE, MICHIGAN
SECTION 6, T49N, R10W
SECTION 1, 2, 11, 12, T49N, R11W

Water is held in Muskallonge Lake by a basin seal

seepage lake

A closed lake and one that presumably loses water mainly by seepage through the walls and floor of its basin; in contrast to a *drainage lake*. A valid objection to this usage and interpretation is that water bodies which receive their input mainly from seepage are *seepage* lakes regardless whether they are *closed* or open.

In Western United States many small lakes or ponds have resulted from seepage from irrigation waters.

See: *drainage lake*

sedimentation of reservoirs

The filling of reservoirs by sediments with special reference to detrital matter carried in by inflowing streams and overland runoff. The terms sedimentation and *silting* are commonly used in the same sense.

See: *sediments, lake*

See: *silting of reservoirs*

sediments (lake)

The term refers to all kinds of deposition on, or comprising, the lake bottom. Sediment the singular usually refers to detrital matter held in suspension, but its usage often is interchangeable with the plural.

seiches

Oscillations, or local rises and falls, in the water level of a lake. The commonest causes of the oscillations or standing waves are: (1) a persistent strong wind and (2) changes in barometric pressure over a portion of the lake. Both may result in piling up of water on shore. On large lakes, and under certain circumstances, the extreme amplitude of a seiche may be 3 or 4 feet or more. Seiches occur on small as well as large lakes, but their amplitudes may be so small that their effects are unnoticed.

semi-public lake

A private lake with provision for permissive public use. The presence of a boat rental or commercial cottages provides limited public access, but this right may be terminated at any time, thereby returning the lake to a private status.

See: *private lake*
public lake

senescent lake

One nearing extinction; especially from filling by the remains of aquatic vegetation.

See: *extinction (lake)*

Senescent lake.

seston

A limnological term which includes both the living organisms, *phytoplankton* and *zooplankton*, and the non-living particles of organic matter floating or held in suspension in the water.

See: *tripton*

settling basin

An artificial basin for collecting the sediment of a river before it flows into a reservoir, and thereby preventing the rapid siltation of the latter. The basin is designed with weirs for drawing off the clear water.

The term is also applied to industrial sedimentation structures used for the removal of pollutant materials from factory effluents.

severed riparian frontage (lake)

Highways and railroads built across bays or arms of lakes frequently sever riparian lands from the lake, if the culverts are not large enough to provide for the passage of boats. The severed riparian frontage has little value unless adequate access to the lake can be obtained.

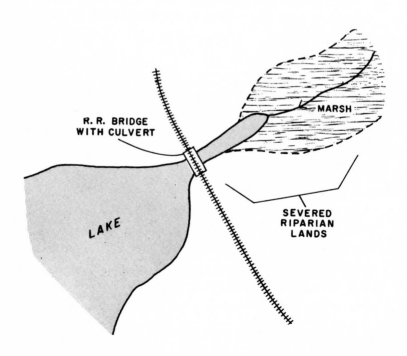

sewage pond

A natural or artificial pond into which sewage is discharged for treatment, or for natural purification. Also called a sewage lagoon.

sewage stabilization lagoon

See: *sewage pond*

sewerage

An inclusive term applied to all effluent carried by a sewerage system. It would include sanitary sewage, industrial wastes and storm sewer water.

shallow lake

Depth figures for what is *shallow* and what is *deep* are comparative and arbitrary. For natural lakes in Michigan, *shallow* generally means depths less than 15 feet.

shallows

The shallower parts of a comparatively deep lake. The depths of water are arbitrary, a few inches to several feet. In some instances of usage of the term, it is merely a synonym for *shoals*.

shanty towns

During the ice fishing season, some lake communities boast of their "shanty towns". However, poetic license is clearly evident, for these towns are actually composed of ice fishing shanties. On certain lakes, many of the required services ordinarily available from stores on shore are available on the ice.

See: *ice shanty*

shape of a lake

The shape of a lake is represented by the drawing of the circumferential line, in its entirety, which marks the position of the shoreline, or the waterline. The shape of a lake is fixed or relatively permanent only where a lake has a fairly constant level. A drop or rise in level may produce a marked change. Some lakes that were originally nearly round or roughly circular, and were given the geographic name Round now bear little resemblance to their original shape, because of lake filling and a drop in lake level.

sheet piling

See: *piling*

shell marl

See: *marl*

shelter lakes

This term has been applied by water-fowl biologists to lakes enclosed by swamps and those largely filled by emergent aquatic vegetation. Such lakes provide a "shelter" or retreat for ducks during periods of stormy and windy weather.

shingle beach

One composed of flattish rounded rock fragments of pebble size or larger. Some of the shingle beaches of Michigan are composed almost entirely of limestone, consisting of rounded flattish pebbles and rounded flat fragments up to 10 and 12 inches or more in length.

shoal island

Some shoals are potential islands — that is at a low level of the lake the shoal becomes exposed and is an island.

shoal water (of a lake)

The water overlying a shoal or shoals; *not* necessarily synonymous with shallow, or shallow water.

In some lake descriptions "shoal areas" are simply the shallow sloping bottoms beginning at the shoreline; or the littoral shelf is called a "shoal".

shoals (inland lakes)

See: *basin* for illustration

Patches of sand, gravel or other hard bottom lying at shallow depths. On most inland lakes *shoal* does not have the same significance in relation to navigation that it has on sea floors and on the Great Lakes, and is therefore, limited to much lesser depths. In some instances of usage, where a lake has considerable variations in depth, *shoals* refers to *shallows* regardless of location and kind of bottom, so that the two terms are practically synonymous. On most inland lakes *shallows* or *shoals* are not more than 10 or 15 feet in depth. In other instances of usage, for deep lakes, a bottom growth of vegetation regardless of depth, is a shoal.

shore

See: *environment* for illustration

Technically the zone of wave action on land; as such *shore* includes beach or strand. Practically, for most lakes, *shore* is simply the land at the contact with the water, and therefore is little more than a line. However, as a geographic term, or as a term in the commerce of land, it can be a border zone for an indeterminate distance back from the water. Also in some instances of usage *shore* includes the shallow water and bottom at the contact with the land, but generally, and more properly, such areas are designated by other terms. In scientific writing, as well as popular

usage *shore* and *shoreline* not uncommonly are used interchangeably, or as terms having the same meaning.

See: *beach*
foreshore
highwater mark
littoral
marsh shore
offshore
shoreline
swamp shore
waterline

shore activity zone

A water zone along the lakeshore beyond which swimming, anchorage of boats, rafts and other structures are
prohibited. The purpose of the shore activity zone is to
reduce hazards resulting from speed boating. The State of
Wisconsin recommends that the zone be 200 feet in width.
Fast boats would be prohibited from entering this zone.

shore classification

See: Appendix.

shore drift

Detritus, mainly sand, carried along shore by currents.
Same as *littoral drift*.

shoreline

See: *environment* for illustration

The points of contact or line between the water and
the land. Both in scientific and popular usage *shoreline* and
shore are commonly interchangeable terms and sometimes
shoreline may mean shore land.

See: *shore*

shoreline acreage ratio

The ratio of linear lake shore line per acre of lake surface. A circular lake would have a low *shoreline acreage ratio*, but as the shoreline becomes sinuous or with the occurrence of bays and arms, the *shoreline acreage ratio* would increase in magnitude.

Artificial lake developers construct lake basins with high *shoreline acreage ratios* so that a maximum number of riparian lots will be available for sale.

From an ecological point of view, lakes with high *shoreline acreage ratios,* usually have more shoal water and therefore provide a greater ecologic potential for fish and wildfowl production.

shoreline development ratio

The ratio, the length of the shoreline to the length of the circumference of a circle whose area is equal to that of the lake. The ratio, from unity, for a lake a perfect circle in shape, or increase over 1, is the shoreline development factor (S. D. F.). The ratio indicates the degree of irregularity of a shoreline.

shore zone (shoreline zone)

The zone directly bordering the lake margin, or shoreline.

show pool

See: *goose pool*

sidd (sudd)

The Arabic word *sidd* is applied to the dense mass of floating vegetation which covers the White Nile and obstructs navigation. By transference, the term may be applied to dense masses of vegetation covering the surface of lakes. *Sidds* include large detached masses of floating bogs, and islands of floating and emergent aquatics such as waterlilies and wild rice. "Blind Sidds" are dense masses of submersed vegetation at very shallow depths that impede boating. Dense masses of aquatic vegetation at the head of an outlet may act as a dam.

Sidds in a Michigan lake.

siltation basin

See: *retarding basin*

silting (of reservoirs)

The filling of reservoirs by sediments carried in by inflowing streams and superficial run-off water. Silting here has no reference exclusively to particles having a definite range in size, as silt, but includes sedimentary particles of all sizes, from colloidal clay to sands.

singing sands

Clean sands on some of the beaches of Lake Michigan emit a high pitched sound when walked over, especially with a scraping gait. Not all beach sands "sing" and the cause when they do remains speculative. The "singing sands" are not peculiar to Michigan; they are common on the coastal beaches of Florida.

Also according to G. P. Merrill, *Rocks, Rock Weathering and Soils,* page 125, on certain Hawaiian beaches the sands, composed largely of shell fragments, give a peculiar crunching sound when walked over and are known as sounding or singing sands.

sink lakes

The term usually refers to lakes or ponds in "lime sinks"

Sink hole, Sunken Lake, Presque Isle County, Michigan. Photo—Scott, I. D., *Inland Lakes of Michigan,* Michigan Geological Survey, Publication No. 30, 1921.

or "sinkholes" due to underground solution of limestone, but the term sink is also applied to other kinds of subsidence depressions.

See: *doline*
sag ponds
solution lakes
suffosion lakes

size (of lakes)

The size of a lake, is usually expressed in terms of the area of the water surface, and does not include volume of water. The size of a lake is generally accepted as an important geographic fact, but actually size may have little real economic significance unless it is supplemented by additional hydrographic, hydrologic, limnologic facts and environmental facts of a socio-economic nature.

See: *area*

skim ice

When freezing first commences on a lake the first ice crystals formed are free floating or weakly attached. This "slushy" layer of "skim" ice can do considerable damage to some kinds of boat hulls.

skin ice

The first film or crust of newly formed ice.

sky lakes

A term sometimes applied to lakes lying at very high altitudes in mountain regions.

sky ponds

Ponds that are dependent upon superficial run-off for their water supply, in contrast to ponds that receive water from springs, seepage and inflowing streams.

slash

A localism in many parts of eastern and southern United States for a marshy, swampy or boggy area often covered with water. The term *slash* has also been applied to a wet lowland lying between parallel beach ridges.

sleek

An oily area on the surface of a lake created where sewage or certain kinds of industrial wastes are discharged; also called slick.

slew

A localism for a wet spot not large enough to be called a swamp or a marsh. Sometimes given as a variant for *slough,* but is not synonymous where *slough* is a term for a body of water in an old river channel.

See: *slough*

slime

Soft fine oozy mud. (Navigation Dictionary, U. S. Hydrographic Office, Bulletin 220) Because of certain other connotations it is not in good standing as a term for lake bottom sediments.

slope (of a lake basin)

Slope consists of two parts, one below the water level of the lake and one above the water level. Slopes above water level extend upward to an even crest of land, or to a run-off divide, and therefore constitute the watershed of a lake.

Slope of the submerged basin may be expressed either in percent or degrees, for the distance between prescribed contours, or as the mean of the entire slope to the maximum depth.

See: *gradient*

slough

In usage throughout the United States this word has several connotations, including standing water bodies. In several parts of the country it is applied to side channels of rivers and to stagnant water bodies in sections of abandoned river channels in alluvial flood plains and deltas. This meaning is common in Michigan, although the occurrences where *slough* appears as a place name on maps are few in number, less than a dozen.

For small water features of a shallow stagnant nature the terms *slough; bayou; dead water; channel; hole; pond; and ox-bow lake* are often used without discrimination. A few instances can be cited where slough appears as a place name, on maps, for water bodies of a kind, which more commonly bears a lake name. These are usually shallow and marshy but are in upland basins, and physiographically are unrelated to the sloughs of river flood plains.

Other applications of slough are to channels of slow moving water in coastal marshlands; and to small marshy and swampy tracts. Marshy depressions or grassy ponds in the prairies of the Midwest were called *sloughs* or *"slews"* by the early explorers and settlers.

sludge

An unprecise, non-technical term in the same category as "mud," "ooze," "slime", "muck" sometimes applied to soft soupy bottom deposits of lakes.

Sludge in the sense of a semifluid mass of solids resulting from the treatment of sewage and the waste from factories and mines may appear as local bottom deposits in polluted lakes. The application of "sludge" to some natural deposits which bear a resemblance to the artificial product is not inapt.

sludge disposal lagoon

In a conventional sewage treatment plant, sludge from the primary settling basin is given a second treatment to further reduce its organic content. The residue from activated sludge treatment is frequently disposed of in old dry meander scars or in a shallow lagoon adjacent to a stream. Location is determined usually by cost of land and isolation from developed areas. During high stream levels, the water effectively cleans these disposal units. Disposal problems are nicely solved but water quality of the stream suffers.

slurry

An appropriate word for lake bottom deposits either inorganic, organic or mixed which are viscous in consistency in the nature of a thick soup.

smirchment, lake

To fill a need and a vacancy in terminology, the word *smirchment* is here proposed as an inclusive term for modification, including additions of extraneous matter to water, bottoms and shorelines, which affect adversely, in a demonstrable way, economic and aesthetic values. The word *pollution* is currently used in an inclusive sense, but it has no precise, sharp meaning, except in terms of some laboratory test, and obviously is not fitting for some of the kinds of lake debasement. The kinds, and causes, of lake *smirchment* are:

(1) sewage and sewage treatment effluents and storm drain effluent;
(2) industrial and mine solid wastes;
(3) acid mine waters;
(4) toxic chemicals and radio-active substances;
(5) used and warm water;

(6) turbidity and siltation from inflowing streams and ditches;

(7) litter and debris on water, ice cover, bottoms and beaches;

(8) defacement of natural shoreline features of wilderness lakes, and their destruction by commercial development of shoreland;

Photo — Michigan Department of Conservation

Modification of shoreline by filling.

(9) diversion of lake water and befoulment from stagnation of water;

(10) defilement of lake vegetation;

(11) surface film of oils, waxes and other hydrocarbons; dissolved gases

(12) pesticides, fungicides and herbicides;

(13) dams and flooding;

(14) noise;

(15) equipment and structures having incompatible color or design;

(16) domestic animals;

(17) objectionable odors;

(18) unusual flavors in fish and game;

(19) runoff from heavily fertilized agricultural lands

snag lake

A lake containing trunks and branches of trees, or the pointed roots of stumps lying on the bottom especially near the shore.

snag shore

Some lakes, especially the wilderness lakes, which are wooded down to the water line, exhibit a shore character-

Lake with a snag shore.

ized by bare tree trunks, lying prostrate in the water, and by branches and roots either attached or detached from the trunks, and either above or below the water level. The trees fall into the water mainly by undercutting of the shore by wave action, but may be overturned and uprooted by ice-shove and wind.

snow-cap

An accumulation of snow on the surface of a frozen over lake. This greatly impedes the penetration of light into the water and materially reduces the ability of plants to replenish the supply of oxygen.

soda lakes

Those whose waters have a high content of sodium carbonate or sodium sulphate. Restricted pretty much to the arid part of Western United States.

soft shore

Shore material composed of peat, muck, mud, or soft marl, in contrast to "hard shore" which is composed of sand, gravel, cobbles, boulders or bed rock.

A soft shore. Here the shore deposit is muck.

soil (of a lake)

"Soil" frequently appears in court decisions with a meaning the same as lake bottom, lake bed or submerged land.

See: *aquasol*
hydrosol

solution lakes

Lakes in depressions, or basins, due to underground solution of rocks, or minerals, and subsequent collapse of the surface. The most common are due to solution of limestone (lime sink lakes of various kinds) gypsum and rock salt. Lakes or ponds also may occupy basins in limestone bed rock formed by solution on the surface.

sound

The term *sound* along sea coasts applied to a relatively long and large body of water, in the nature of a strait, connecting two larger bodies of water. It may lie between an island and the mainland. However, both in place names and colloquially the term is used loosely and not consistently distinguished from other hydronyms such as *bay, pond, lake, lagoon, river* and estuary; and is sometimes applied to short connecting channels in a salt marsh.

Sound appears only occasionally in place names on inland lakes. It may apply to a stretch of water between a long island and the mainland; or to a long bay or arm of a lake.

space consumption

The comparative amount of space on the water surface of a lake, and on the shore required for a particular use. For example, the space required by a swimmer, or for still fishing is relatively small; that for motor boating and water skiing relatively large.

Photo – Michigan Department of Conservation

Lake used for bathing and swimming; the space requirement per person is relatively small.

Water skiing. Large amount of space consumed.

Photo – Michigan Department of Conservation

Sunbathing is enjoyed by all age groups.

304

Photo – Michigan Department of Conservation

Still fishing.

spate ponds

This term *spate pond* is here proposed as a fitting one for standing water bodies which result from natural floodings of land surfaces. The floodings may result from either brief or extended periods of rain; from overflow of rivers; from storm waves extending over low shore land; or from deluges of any kind. Some "spate ponds" are no more than ephemeral puddles, or shallow sheets of water which can be dessicated in a few days or a few weeks; but others may remain for considerable periods of time for example in deep depression which happen to be filled with floodwaters; and those in the form of stagnant pools in dense swamps.

spatterdock

A common name for species of *Nuphar* also known as yellow pond lily. Some lakes are almost completely covered

Spatterdock partly filling a lake.

by pads of this plant, so it becomes one of the principal sources of filling, resulting in lake extinction.

spile dams

Dams constructed by driving posts, or other piling into the soil. Sometimes stones are placed in the spaces between the piling, and sometimes the piling is covered by planking. A number of such dams were made in the northern part of Michigan during the lumbering days 1870-1920, and in a few locations remains of the dams and impoundments still exist.

spit

A depositional feature consisting of detritus, or sediments, carried out from shore by currents and laid down in the form of an embankment. The spit has one end attached to the shore and the other terminates in open water. Sometimes the end is recurved toward the shore forming a *hook*.

"Spits" may be cuspate in form, and so the distinction between a *cusp* and a *spit* may become a bit blurred.

spoil (spoils)

The material removed in excavation or dredging in the construction of access canals, boat or navigation channels, drainage ditches and in the rejuvenation of senescent lakes. In its disposal it is often left as banks alongside the ditches excavated; sometimes used as fill for the improvement of cottage sites on swampy shores; sometimes dumped in the open water of the lake with results which may be harmful.

spread

The term "spread" or "widespread" is a localism applied to a water feature which has resulted from expansion in width of a stream due to some natural obstruction in its course, to choking by aquatic vegetation or to filling of its bed by sediment. The stream widens out to form a marsh, or shallow marshy lake, in which its channel is either lost or divided into a number of small distributaries. A "spread" may hinder, or prevent, continuous boating or canoeing. Spread in the sense stated remains in current usage in Michigan and appears in place names in several locations. It is also in use in Wisconsin and appears very sparingly in place names in a few other States.

spring lake

A spring lake or *limnokrene*, is a pool created by the emergence of a bold spring; or a lake that receives its entire input directly from a spring or springs. In popular usage a *spring* or *spring-fed* lake is one that has visible flowing springs (as opposed to seeps) on its shores, or one that is fed by springs rising from the lake bottom. However, the term is often loosely applied; some so called spring lakes receive only a minor part of their water from springs, and for some, the "springs" are purely mythical. Springs may raise the temperature of the water in winter and prevent complete freezing over; or on the other hand in summer may lower the temperature and produce a "cold water" lake.

spring overturn

A phenomenon that may take place in a lake in early spring. Beginning with the melting of the ice and warming of the surface water, and a change in density, a general circulation or mixing of the water from top to bottom takes place resulting in physical and chemical uniformity which may be referred to as the initial phase of summer stagnation.

stabilization lagoon
See: *sewage pond*

stack
A relatively small projecting mass of rock, various in shape which has been detached from the mainland cliff by wave erosion. The *stack* is present as an island along the shores only of very large lakes subject to powerful wave action.

stage
In Hydrology, the height of the water surface above or below an arbitrary datum; a gage height. As a physiographic term as in the "stage of development of a shore line" stage refers to a period or phase in the cycle of erosion which may be expressed for example as the *youthful stage* or mature stage. The final period in the life history of a lake may be called a stage of extinction. Also former levels of a lake, marking periods in its geological history, are called *stages* and often given the geographic name of the ancient predecessor lake, as for example, the Algonquin Stage of Lake Michigan.

See: *level*

standing crop
The biomass, or total quantity of living organisms in the lake at a particular time.

standing water
Surface water that has no perceptible flow and remains in place; includes some types of lakes and ponds, and inclosed water in marshes and swamps.

See: *lentic*

static lakes

In relation to water level, or elevation of the lake surface, *static* lakes are those which remain at a constant
level; or those that are subject to only relatively small
changes in level throughout the year. The opposed group
is astatic, and includes those lakes which are subject to
wide fluctuations in level. In relation to economics of lake
use, constancy of level is generally desirable; wide fluctuations, especially low levels, can have serious economic
consequences, especially where the lake affected is very
shallow, and where the bottom beginning at the shoreline
has only a slight gradient.

Constancy of levels is not desirable under all circumstances. In some artificial floodings, subject to control by
dams, or other engineering measures, levels may be purposely lowered or raised in accordance with the needs of
management.

stocked lake

A lake which has been planted with fish of a desirable
species.

stonewort

A common name for species of *Chara*.

See: *Chara*

storage reservoir

In a storage reservoir water is impounded back of a
high dam and held for later use. Storage reservoirs are
subject to wide variations in level, and this affects adversely their potential value for some recreational uses.

See: *run of the river reservoir*

storm beach

See: *beach profile* for illustration

The term *storm beach* can have two connotations: (1) that part of the beach which lies above the level of the advance of normal waves, and therefore subject to wave action only during storms; (2) the whole beach as it appears immediately after a violent storm, and characterized by modifications involving either removal or deposition of beach sands; and commonly by beach pools and lodgement of floating debris.

Storm beach, east end of Lake Michigamme. From Scott, I.D., *Inland Lakes of Michigan*, Michigan Geological Survey, Publication No. 30, 1921, page 300.

strand

The strip at the base of shore cliff, or along shore, that is lapped by waves. Strand and beach can have the same meaning, or strand can include beaches, but commonly *beach* is the term applied to any sandy or pebbly part of the shore and especially so if that part has a recreational use.

stranded lake frontage

Lots, which according to plat surveys originally extended to the water line, but no longer do so because of a recession of the lake. In the parlance of the real estate developer, such lots are designated *stranded lake frontage*.

stranded peninsula

A peninsula physically attached to a territory of one governmental entity but legally under the jurisdiction of another unit of government. In this respect it is stranded from its parent authority and can be reached only by boat or by traversing over the territory of another unit of government.

strandline

Shoreline of a beach, on any shoreline. Frequently used in lake descriptions.

strath lake

A lake formed in connection with a strath type of alluvial filling. Where a lake is long and narrow and has a stream entering at one end the sediment carried in may not be deposited in a delta form, but may fill the breadth of the lake as an alluvial plain. Sometimes a lake is formed between levees of alluvium and the original lake shore.

stratified flow

When a difference exists between the density of the inflowing water and that of a lake or reservoir, heavier inflowing water, such as that of a cold or turbid stream, may sink and produce an "underflow" or interflow and lighter water, such as fresh water flowing into a saline body, may remain on the surface producing an "overflow".

stratified lakes

In deeper lakes, especially in temperate regions, the water from top to bottom exhibits differences in temperatures. Lakes in which the water occurs in thermal layers are called *stratified lakes*. In thermal stratification, the upper layer is known as the *epilimnion;* the next stratum is known as the *thermocline;* and the lower-most layer of water is the *hypolimnion.*

In addition to temperature, stratification of the water of lakes may also be caused by differences at different depths in amount of suspended silt, and in amounts of dissolved salts. In some reservoirs clear water overlies "muddy" water, because the suspended silt, due to greater density, has sunk to the bottom. Also it sometimes happens that a surface layer of fresh water overlies salt water.

See: *destratification*

stripmine ponds

In localities where coal has been mined by surface stripping, often ponds accumulate in unfilled excavations and appear in impoundments created by piling of spoil. In abandoned strip mine areas some of these ponds have a permanence, size and total area sufficient to give them a considerable ecologic and economic significance.

See: *artificial lakes, ponds*

subaquatic plants

Emergent plants; or hydrophytes which are not submersed.

subaquatic soil

One permanently covered with water; a lake bottom that supports plant growth is a subaquatic soil.

subaqueous terrace
See: *basin* for illustration
See: *littoral shelf*

sublacustrine
Applicable to features beneath the lake water, or on the lake bottom.

sublimation losses (lake)
Water lost from the frozen surface of lake by the combined effect of solar radiation and wind circulation. Water molecules from ice and snow crystals change directly into a gas without passing through an intermittent water stage.

Accurate measurement of *sublimation losses* is difficult, but estimates for Michigan and Wisconsin range about 4 inches annually.

sublittoral
See: *beach profile* for illustration
In limnological terminology, the *sublittoral* is the transition zone in the lake bottom lying between the *littoral* and the *profundal*. The *profundal* is the depth at which aquatic vegetation is absent.
See: *littoral*
profundal

sublittoral shelf
See: *littoral shelf*

submerged aquatic plant
A plant whose main parts grow under the water surface. Some species may have floating leaves or produce fruiting bodies that extend above the water surface but the main portions of the plant are submerged: *Chara sp;*

Anacharis (Elodea) sp.; Ceratophyllum sp. and *Potomogeton sp.* are common submerged aquatics in lakes. Also called submersed plant.

submerged land (inland lakes)

Lake bottom land, or that land covered by water when the lake is at its *ordinary high water mark;* or at its legal level. The bottom may be temporarily exposed due to lake recession, but remains *submerged land* in a legal sense.

The status of land covered by the water of artificial impoundments, that underlying large reservoirs, floodings and flowages, is not uniformly established, but on the contrary is subject to different rulings in individual cases. Also problems may arise in the interpretation of the word *submerged* where land is flooded from natural causes, as by natural dams, land subsidence, or the plugging of subterranean outlets. Land may be covered by some forms of standing water in swamps and marshes and yet in a legal, sense may not be *submerged land.*

See: *recession*
reliction

submerged platform

See: *littoral shelf*

submerged terrace

See: *basin* for illustration
beach profile for illustration
littoral shelf

subsaline water

With reference, to ponds, lakes, sloughs and marshes, water that is slightly less salty or lower in salinity than sea water.

substrate (lake)

A term used by ecologists for the medium in which, or place where, organisms grow or live. The lake bottom deposits of various kinds constitute various kinds of substrates. Also the under surface of a floating leaf of an aquatic plant may be a *substrate* for organisms.

subsequent island (lake)

One formed subsequent to, or after, the formation of the lake. For example, those formed by the accumulations of lake sediments, and those resulting from changes in lake level.

sudd

See: *sidd*

suds

Where lake waters naturally contain a large amount of organic matter in suspension or solution, or are polluted

Photo – Michigan Department of Conservation

Suds on a Michigan lakeshore.

with sewage, waves often leave a conspicuous and sometimes objectionable ridge of foam, or masses of "suds", on the shoreline.

See: *foam*

suffosion lakes

Bodies of water occupying depressions due to a subsidence of the land surface. The depressions may result from cave-ins of mine workings; subsidence due to exhaustion of water, or petroleum by pumping, from porous strata. The suffosion may be a natural process such as the underground solution of limestone, salt and gypsum, leaving caverns whose roofs subsequently collapse and produce sink hole lakes.

sump

A term used, on Reclamation Projects in Western United States, for sub-basins which serve the purpose of collecting drainage water. The water may be subsequently used for irrigation, or may be retained in the *sump* in the interest of wild fowl conservation.

An old English and Scottish provincial word for a muddy inlet, or a cove. Also means a stagnant pool or puddle.

summer kill

Mortality of fish and other aquatic animals in lakes, during summer, that may result from such causes as algal blooms, oxygen depletion and temperature changes. In the northern latitudes, the danger from pollutants is greater in summer than in winter.

sunken islands

A localism for the crests of knobs, basin divides or other high configuration features of a lake basin, covered only to a shallow depth by water. These features were never originally above water level, and therefore, are not due to subsidence. They are distinguished from shoals, "blind" islands, and shallow underwater features due to lake filling.

surf

The effect produced by the break of a wave as it enters shallow water or a shallow shore zone. The effect, a rush of water between the breaker and the shoreline, sound and foam, is not appreciable except on the seashore or shores of very large bodies of inland water. Surf is reckoned as an intangible or aesthetic value.

Inland waters (lakes and streams) may be used for surfing if a stern wave of sufficient height can be created by a boat equipped with powerful outboard motors. The *carrying capacity* of a lake is greatly reduced by this specialized sport and damage may result to other boats and shore as a result of the wake.

surface waters

In the interpretation of hydrologists, *surface water* is that lying on the surface of the land in contrast to underground water. Thus lakes and streams are regarded as *surface water*. However, in some legal interpretations *surface water* is restricted to *diffused water*, and therefore lakes and streams are excluded in the definition.

See: *diffused water*

surfing (lake)

A relatively new inland water sport involving the use of a high boat wake, simulating ocean surf. If a square stern boat is heavily loaded and equipped with a motor of sufficient horsepower, the resulting wake may be used for surfboard riding.

swag

This localism is common in some parts of the United States for small shallow pockets or closed depressions in flat or gentle rolling terrain. In the bottom lands of the

Lower Mississippi, "swags" on ridges are filled with water for a part of the year and constitute temporary ponds. *Swag* and *sag* are often used interchangeably.

See: *sag ponds*

swale

In relation to lake physiography this term has been applied to a wet depression between beach ridges.

swamp

The term *swamp* has no accepted precise or technical meaning; it is a word that has taken on a number of connotations in literature and common speech according: to time of its use; geographic locality; context in literary usage; statutes and court decisions. The term has been used comprehensively for all forms of wet land, but a commonly accepted distinction is that *swamp* connotes wet land that supports tree vegetation. As such, *swamp* may be merely wet land, that with a miry soil and a shallow water table; or it may be a feature intermittently covered with water; or one permanently covered with water; as for example some of the cypress swamps of the southern states of the United States. Instances may be cited, where in the processes of nature, open sheets of water have been converted into tree covered swamps; and conversely true swamps, by inundation or by subsidence, have been converted into tree covered lakes. Thus the distinction between a *swamp* and a *lake* may become shadowy.

See: *bog*
marsh
morass
wetlands

(For illustration see page 320.)

Water covered type of swamp.

swamp shore

A descriptive term applied where the shoreland bordering the water line of a lake is wet and covered with tree vegetation. In contrast to marsh shore; to dryland shore, and to highland shore.

swarm of lakes

The term applies to a large number (hundreds) of lakes closely associated in a region, or to a large cluster. "Swarms" are fairly common in the Lake States and Canada, both on moraines and outwash plains; in a number

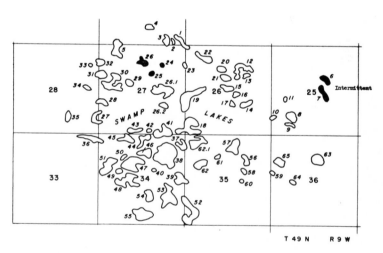

A swarm of lakes. Swamp Lakes, Luce County, Michigan.

of localities 20 or more lakes may be clustered in an area of 10 square miles or less.

See: *chain of lakes*
gang of lakes

swash
> The water carried upshore from the break of a wave. Also run up.

swash marks
> A shoreline micro feature — marking the farthest advance of swash.
>> See: *swash*
>> *uprush*

swash zone
> The area, on a beach, above the water line, covered by uprush water.
>> See: *uprush*

swatch
> A channel between an offshore bar and the shoreline.

sweet gas
> A localism applied to methane and other hydrocarbon gases escaping from holes cut in the ice cover of shallow eutrophic lakes. The gas from decomposition of organic material normally escapes notice during ice free periods, but during a freeze-over it is concentrated under the ice.

sweet water
> In its most common usage, the term, means "fresh water" as opposed to "salt or brackish" water.

swell
> A wave which continues after the wind has ceased.
>> See: *wave*

swimmers itch

A rash produced by a parasitic flat worm (in the cercarial stage of its life) which penetrates the skin of bathers. Snails are hosts for the parasite. Copper sulphate is commonly used to control the snail population.

swimming island

An island dedicated to the common use and enjoyment of riparians on an artificial lake. These islands are sometimes called *swimming islands* and are surveyed but not platted for sale. Jurisdiction over these islands frequently passes on to a lake association after initial development has been completed.

synergism, pollution

In pollution the sum of two toxicants reacting together, may be greater than the effect of the sum of the two acting separately or independently.

See: *antagonism, pollution*

tail race

See: *head race*

tailings ponds

Enclosures, or basins, constructed for the disposal of mine tailings, the fine rock waste in washings flowing from mills after the grinding and treatment of ores. The "ponds", acting as settling basins are intended to prevent contamination of streams and other natural waters. Usually they are no more than watery wastes and serve no other useful purpose.

(See illustration on page 324.)

Photo – Michigan Department of Conservation

A tailings pond at Book Mine, Alpha, Michigan.

tank

A term for a pond especially in the semi-arid and arid parts of western United States. A *tank* may be a natural pool, but is usually an artificial impoundment of an intermittent stream, or of surface runoff, made to serve primarily as a water supply for livestock. Also *estanque*, stank, and stanch. The term *tank* rarely appears in usage east of the Mississippi; although it is an old and obsolete English and Scottish word for a pond, or pool.

> See: *charco*
> *dugout pond*

tarn

The term is in current use by geologists and geomorphologists, and usually designates relatively small, deep lakes in high mountain areas, especially those that have been glaciated.

The term has long been used in the northern part of England for lakes, or pools, some of which may be in moors.

In Michigan, C. A. Davis (Michigan Geological Survey, Annual Report, 1906, Peat, page 116) proposed the word *tarn* for the landlocked lakes of the state. It serves a useful purpose as a name for lakes or pools, especially those without inlet or outlet streams, within swamp, marsh, bog, or muskeg tracts. Under these circumstances, it should be given an attributive, for example, *bog tarn*, *marsh tarn*.

In reference to lakes in depressions in glacial drift in northeastern United States, I. C. Russell (*Lakes of North America*, page 16) states: "They vary in size from mere *tarns* to splendid water sheets many square miles in area." One may infer that tarn is a term for a small lake. Geologists and geomorphologists would prefer that tarn apply

to small lakes in mountain regions, especially those occupying cirques. However in usage it is not so restricted, in
fact any small lake may be called a tarn.

tectonic lakes
Lakes in basins produced by earth movements; uplift,
subsidence and faulting.

tellurometer
An electronic surveying device used for measuring distances between lake shores, by use of micro waves similar
to radar.

telmaro
A term coined from the Greek words for marsh and
river.

A river, or other watercourse traversing a peat marsh
or peat swamp, in contradistinction to a stream entrenched
in a floodplain of alluvial deposition.

The streams have their source within the marsh or
swamp, from a lake or from springs on the marsh border,
have few or no tributaries from the adjacent highland and
hence carry very little mineral detritus in suspension. The
banks are very low, or the stream level may be nearly flush
with the swamp level. The channels may be either very
shallow or fairly deep. Some *telmaros* are no more than the
connecting fluves of chain lakes. Also in some instances a
large stream may have a marsh flood plain which is super-
imposed on an original, or earlier, plain of mineral soil.
This condition happens where the stream flow has been
backed up from some natural circumstance thus creating
a permanent flooding favorable for the growth of aquatic
plants and eventual accumulation of peat.

temporary lake

A basin or depression that holds water for only a short period, or during a season in contrast to a permanent lake, one that retains its water throughout the year.

See: *intermittent lake*

tension crack ice

Openings resulting from tension cracks on frozen lakes quickly freeze but remain evident unless covered by snow. The structure of this *tension crack ice* differs from normal lake ice; it may be clear enough to enable fishermen to examine the lake bottom.

territorial water

Surface water, stream or lake, within territorial jurisdiction of the Federal Government or a State.

test well (lake)

A well installed adjacent to a lake to determine the relationship between the ground water level and the lake level.

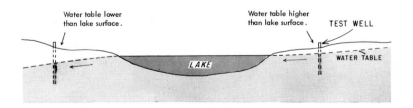

Test Well

thaw lakes

Lakes in shallow depressions resulting from unequal thawing of permafrost in arctic regions. Such lakes have also been given the name thermokarst; and subsidence depressions due to thawing also have been called *kettles* and *cave-ins*.

thermocline

In thermally stratified lakes, the layer below the *epilimnion*. It is the stratum in which there is a rapid rate of decrease in temperature with depth; a minimum of one degree Centigrade per meter in depth.

See: *stratified lakes*

thermokarst

See: *thaw lake*

thinolite

A crystalline calcareous tufa. Notable deposits were formed on the shore of ancient Lake Lahontan in the Great Basin.

till ball

See: *clay balls*

tiphic

Pertaining to a pond. *(Klugh)*

tombolo

A sand or gravel bar which ties an island to another island or to the mainland. Under certain conditions the island may be attached by two bars, which in turn may enclose a lake or lagoon.

tombolo island

A term for an island tied to the shore, or mainland, by one or more tombolos, which are bars or spits which rise above the water level. Under certain conditions, where there are two bars they may enclose a lake or lagoon.

See: *presque isle*

A double tombolo connecting a small rock island to Sandpoint, Sandpoint Island, Rainy Lake, Ontario, Canada. Photo by Bruce Caldwell, Department of Lands and Forests, Fort Frances, Ontario, Canada.

train of lakes

A small number of lakes, 4 to 5 to 10 to 12, arranged in a linear pattern, relatively small in size, more or less uniformly spaced and tied together by sections of a stream or by narrow channels.

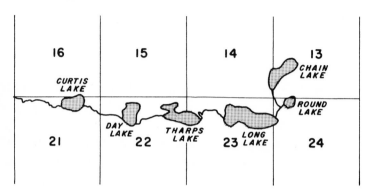

A train of lakes. T17N; R14W; Cass County, Michigan.

transient beach

A sand beach, one whose sand covering is subject to removal by the wave action of storms, leaving usually, a beach of cobbles and boulders; however. the alteration is not necessarily permanent. Often the sand is restored in a short time by littoral current deposition.

transient boat

A portable boat or one that is not moored or anchored solely for use at one location. The availability of public access sites to surface water has provided an ever expanding market for portable boats. New trailer design is so efficient that even cabin type craft may be easily and safely transported to water recreation sites for weekend use.

See: *moored boat*
fleet boats

transparency

The transparency of lake water may be measured by the use of the *Secchi* disk. A disk with alternate black and white quadrants, 20 cm in diameter is lowered in the water until it disappears from view, and then raised until it reappears; the mean depth is called the *Secchi disk transparency*.

transpiration losses (lake)

Water consumed by emergent and floating lake plants, voided as gas through specialized leaf cells. Measurement of transpiration losses is difficult but estimates for the Lake States region range around 36 to 48 inches. In California, giant tule may utilize as much as 21 feet of water annually.

transverse bar

A bar which extends at nearly right angles from the shoreline.

traverse

The Traverse is a name given to a pass between two islands in the Lake of the Woods, Ontario, Canada.

tripton

The non-living particles of organic matter held in suspension in the water.

See: *seston*

trolling water

In lakes, deep weed and snag-free water.

trophic lakes

See: *dystrophic*
eutrophic
oligotrophic

trout lake

By legal definition: "A lake in which brook trout, brown trout or rainbow trout are the predominating species of game fish found therein" (Act 165, P. A. 1929. 301.10 Trout Lake, Michigan). In practice, the term may be applied to a lake in which trout are present, but not necessarily in predominant numbers.

Trust Doctrine (pertaining to lakes)

Under the doctrine of trust it is implied that natural resources are held in trust by the State, and that the State as trustee, has a duty and obligation to conserve and preserve them in the public interest. This doctrine, or philosophy, may be accepted in theory under one set of conditions, and strongly opposed, in practice, under another set of circumstances. Ownership by the Lake States of lake bottom and rights to control the use of waters along the shoreline of the Great Lakes is well established. However, proposals to extend such ownership and rights to apply to all inland lakes are likely to meet with strong objections or counter arguments because of the long accepted belief, bolstered by court decision, that individual riparians own the lake bottoms and that private owners have the right of control over private lakes.

tundra lakes

Innumerable pools and some lakes occur in tundras in Alaska and Canada in the early summer and some persist throughout the summer. This type of tundra consists of a thin cover of peat over bare rock, mostly bed rock, and the pools and lakes are mostly in basins in the rock. Many are enclosed by low banks of peat often undercut and overhanging.

See: *thaw lakes*

turbidity

The degree of opaqueness of the water due to the amount of fine matter in suspension. The particles that cause turbidity may also determine apparent color.

Carp, suckers and sturgeon commonly extract food from the bottom deposits of lakes. Their feeding involves sucking, digging and rooting which creates localized turbidity, and this in turn may adversely affect the growth of certain aquatic plants. Their feeding action may also be considered as a form of cultivation that occurs in shallow water that is otherwise protected from wave and current action.

See: *color*
transparency

turbidity currents

Density currents due to suspended silt.

See: *density currents*
stratified flow

turbidity fan

A localized fan shaped area of turbid water at the mouth of an influent or adjacent to an eroding lake bank.

Turbidity fan resulting from leveling and clearing of lakeshore.

turlough

A term of Irish origin for a seasonal lake, one that contains water only during the winter; a *land lake*.

two-story lake

A term for a lake which has a surface layer of warm water and a deep layer of cold water. In relation to fishing such a lake may for example support a population of bass and bluegills in the "upper story" and trout and cisco in the "lower story".

under-developed lake

As an economic entity, or in its social significance, a lake is *under-developed*, when the number of residents on its water frontage and the adjacent shoreland, or the amount of resort or commercial development, and use of beaches is less than the carrying capacity.

Rural township and county officials frequently promote and encourage lake development in order to increase the local tax base.

See: *carrying capacity* (recreational)

undercut bank

A bank, or cliff, that has been excavated at the base by wave erosion, leaving an overhanging face or front.

underflow

See: *stratified flow*

undertow

Commonly regarded as a dangerous bottom current created by the return seaward, or lakeward, of water piled up on the shore by waves. However, the notion that bathers are pulled beneath the water by "undertow" as a bottom current, is not supported by any conclusive evidence. Under certain conditions strong *rip currents*, which are surface or near surface currents, are set up in the return of breaker waters, and drownings are due to bathers being caught in strong rips, rather than in a bottom current or undertow. "Undertow" is a cause of drownings on seacoasts and beaches of the Great Lakes, but the forces set up by the return of wave water on the beaches of inland lakes are seldom sufficiently strong to be a menace to bathers and swimmers.

underwater borrow pit
See: *borrow pit pond*

Underwater borrow pit. Excavation for sand and gravel in foreground; older part in background, reshaped and used for bathing.

underwater lands
Lake bottomlands that are normally covered with water.
See: *submerged land*

underwater lot
Under a Michigan statute (P. A. 1899 Act 175), underwater lots were surveyed in the St. Clair Flats area for lease to individuals for recreational purposes. Many of these lots have subsequently been developed by filling and present an interesting illustration of elaborate and costly, but economic, use of water surface, marsh and delta lands.

See: *public highway*

undeveloped access (lake)
On some lake plats, walkways and roadways down to the shoreline that were formally dedicated for the exclusive use of the lot owners or for public use were never developed. Large trees, brush and steep banks have discouraged use from becoming established. Frequently, the adjacent property owners mutually divide these undeveloped access ways and fence them to discourage use. The legal procedure to vacate these access ways is cumbersome.

undeveloped shore
A shore which remains largely in a natural state, or without any man-made modifications for recreational or commercial uses.

unlimited access (lake)
Public roads, public parks, and right of ways for fishing, granting public access to lakes often allow unlimited numbers of people to enter onto lake waters at any time. Public access to lakes not entirely publicly owned may be socially desirable, but also the private riparian owners have a right to management that restricts use in accordance with the carrying capacity of the lake.

unnamed lakes

Many very small or isolated bodies of surface water have not assumed importance enough to merit a geographic name. Locally these lakes and ponds may be designated by names but these do not have any official standing. If the name is included on a map, recorded on a plat or mentioned in a newspaper it may eventually become the accepted or official name.

See: *names of lakes*

unplatted island

A term applied to lake islands (usually less than 50 acres) which were not subdivided during the General Land Office survey of the Public Domain. By unplatted is meant that no section or other land lines were established although the island might have been located and described. The fact that an island was unplatted in the survey, has been a deciding factor in its disposition and ownership. In some instances the Federal Government retained ownership, in others these islands were granted to the States.

upper, middle and lower lake

Where two or more lakes are connected by a flowing stream or channel, that lake located farthest upstream (or up gradient, regardless of compass direction) is commonly designated upper; for example Upper Straits Lake.

uprush

The rush of water up the shore following the plunge of the wave.

Uprush on wide sand beach.

uvala

A compound depression of dolines.
See: *doline*

V-bar

See: *cuspate foreland*

varve

A thin layer in lake bottom sediments which represents an annual deposition. Usually it consists of a lower
part which represents summer deposition, and an upper
part finer grained and one sometimes almost entirely
organic, which represents winter deposition.

vernal autumnal ponds

Those that contain water in the spring season, dry up
in the summer, and again contain water in the autumn.

vernal ponds
Those that contain water, for limited periods, in the spring.

vertical lakeshore development
The occupance of shoreland may be greatly increased by vertical forms of development. Multi-storied hotels, motels and marinas accommodate more people per unit of frontage than conventional cottages.

vicinage (lake)
See: *environment* (lake) for illustration

The land back of the shoreline for an indeterminate distance. It is the bordering land which by its nature affects the economic or aesthetic value of the lake; or the lake itself may be a determining factor in the kind of use made of the contiguous land. Thus the *vicinage* becomes the extent of the area which affects or is affected by the lake as a focal center.

See: *environment* (lake)

virus
An extremely small living organism or non-living particle; it is sometimes found in lake water. Viruses are so small that they may pass through a porcelain filter. Sewage treatment plants are not designed to remove viruses, some of which may cause disease in both plants and animals.

Tests for viruses are so difficult and costly as to limit their widespread use. If water tests show the presence of coliform bacteria or detergents from household wastes, the presence of viruses should also be suspected.

Due to their minute size viruses may easily move through soil and geologic formations to pollute lakes and wells. This aspect of pollution will require considerable research to evaluate its potential threat.

vly (vley; vlei; vlaie; fly)

The word *vly* (with variant spellings) appears in some instances of usage as a name for a marshy feature or water-covered lowland, and for a shallow pond. In geographic range in the United States it is pretty much restricted to New York and New Jersey.

Many of the *vlys* of the Adirondack region of New York represent the sites of lakes, or ponds, which have become extinct by filling by aquatic vegetation.

volume (of a lake)

The surface area times the depth. Where a contour map of the submerged part of a lake basin is available the total volume is the sum of the volumes for each contour stratum. A formula for calculating the *volume* of a stratum is $V = \frac{1}{3}(A_1 + A_2 + \sqrt{A_1 A_2})h$. Where A_1 is the area of the upper surface and A_2 the area of the lower surface of a stratum and h is the height of the stratum.

wake

The track left in the water by a moving boat. Waves generated by fast boats can accelerate erosion, particularly on the banks of narrow channels, and sometimes cause damage to boats tied to docks.

walk-in access

A public access way, to lakes or other waters, designed only for foot travel. The walk-in access is provided primarily for the use of fishermen; canoes, or other small boats may be carried in.

walled lakes

Lakes bordered on shore, by low walls, or sometimes only remnants, composed of boulders and cobbles. The "walls" are the result of ice-shove, due to the expansion of ice of frozen-over lakes, which picks up and shoves stones lying in the shallow bottom of the lake and on the shore, eventually forming an embankment. A technical account of this phenomenon is given in the Ninth Annual Report, Michigan Geological Survey, 1907, Surface Geology of Michigan by A. C. Lane pages 104-107.

See: *ice rampart*
ice shove

wallows

See: *buffalo wallows*

warm water, and cold water lakes

In the absence of accepted temperature criteria for determining in which group a particular lake falls, such a grouping of lakes, except for extremes, is arbitrary and has little scientific or practical value. Fishery biologists sometimes designate trout lakes (and streams) as "cold" water; and bass and bluegill lakes (and streams) as "warm".

waste stabilization lagoon

A shallow artificial pond constructed for the stabilization of industrial wastes.

Water

This word sometimes is the generic, replacing *lake*, in place names of water bodies although such use in the United States is infrequent.

water bloom

A prolific growth of plankton. A bloom of algae may be so dense that it imparts a greenish yellowish, or brownish color to the water. The growth may be so concentrated in some parts of a lake that it intereferes with swimming

Algal bloom concentrated in bay of a lake.

and boating. The algae not only imparts a disagreeable odor, but may be a cause of fish mortality, and some species may be poisonous to cattle and ducks and a menace to drinking water supplies.

See: *Algae*
diatoms

water chinquapin

A water lily, *Nelumbo lutea,* which has yellow flowers and leaves raised well above the water surface. The seeds and tubers are edible. This plant appears in lakes in the eastern part of the United States. Also known as American lotus.

water front

That portion of the shoreline that has been intensively developed for commercial purposes.

See: *frontage*

water hyacinth

A floating aquatic, genus *Eichornia (Piaropus),* characterized by rosettes of stalked large leaves. In some Southern states, especially Louisiana and Florida, it forms an almost complete cover over the surface of lakes and streams and seriously interferes with boating and other recreational uses of the waters.

water prairie

See: *wet prairie*

water quality, lakes

The graded value of a single property, or the characteristics as a whole, in relation to a particular use. The property, or constituents, determining quality may be either organic or inorganic; chemical or physical; and a quality may be fairly constant or may be highly variable. The quality of lake waters may be natural or may be the result of modifications by man's activities. The water is graded, or quality expressed in relation to its use for (1) drinking; (2) industrial purposes; (3) recreation; (4) irrigation and agriculture.

In many instances water quality criteria have been established for specific uses and when these criteria are subject to exacting measurement or evaluation, water quality assumes a more realistic meaning.

water trails

See: *canoe trail*

water hole

In usage the term is pretty well restricted to the arid and semi-arid parts of western United States. It is applied to very small depressions or "holes", which contain water a part of the year, or yearlong. The water may be derived from seeps; or the "water hole" may be merely a pool in the otherwise dry bed of a stream.

waterline (of a lake)

See: *basin* for illustration
beach profile for illustration
The line of contact between the still water of a lake or pond and the bordering land. The waterline marks the actual level at a particular time, and therefore is not necessarily the equivalent of or synonomous with *high water mark, ordinary high water mark, mean water level,* or *shoreline.*

watershed (lake)

The whole surface drainage area that contributes water to a lake.

See: *hydrographic basin*

waterway

A navigable body of water, natural or artificial, which serves as a water highway or water road. Ordinarily the term implies that the water body is used by vessels engaged in trade or commerce, but sole use by pleasure boats is not precluded. Under the definition many navigable lakes, either as an individual body or as a chain, as well as rivers, straits, sounds; passes, channels, or; cuts and canals qualify as *waterways*.

In the commercial development of stream frontage adjacent to lakes, shallow inflowing streams are often dredged for short distances from the lake and called "waterways" although their only purpose is to provide boat access to the lake. A connecting waterway between two lakes can afford easy access by boat to either of the lakes, and for this reason riparian land along the waterway can command high prices per front foot for cottages, permanent residences and commercial structures.

See: *channel*

Photo – Michigan Tourist Council

Connecting waterway between Burt and Mullet Lakes, Michigan.

wave

A wave is an undulation or ridge on a water surface. Waves commonly result from the force of wind currents upon minor irregularities on the lake surface. The size of the wave or magnitude is directly related to the intensity and constancy of the wind. In deep water, movement is restricted to the vertical oscillation of water particles, but when the wave reaches shallow water it breaks and the horizontal onrush of water results in horizontal movement that can move bottom materials on to the shore and off from the shore. Wave action can result in erosion of the shore or in damage to shore installations.

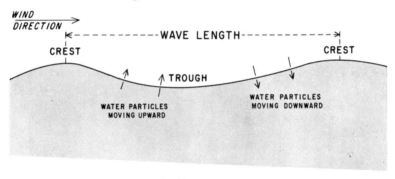

Oscillatory wave.

Wave action on inland lakes is of much less magnitude than on oceans, but it still represents a significant factor in the value and use of lake environment. Geologically the origin of beaches depends upon wave action and the resultant erosion and sorting action of moving water. Aesthetically, wave appearance and sounds contribute to the enjoyment of the lakescape. On larger lakes, waves may hinder or restrict various uses of the water surface.

Waves may also be created by various other forces: landslides; earthquakes; barometric pressure; ship's wake.

See: *seiche*

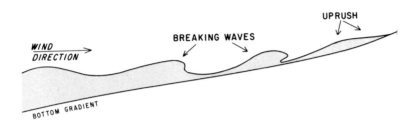

Wave of translation.

wave breakers

Lines of large stones, piling, logs or other material placed at right angle to the prevailing wind and usually submerged to a shallow depth designed to protect shallow shoals, shore bottoms and shorelines from strong wave action.

wave-built terrace

See: *littoral shelf*

wave-cut terrace

See: *littoral shelf*

weed beds

Associations or communities of aquatic plants occurring as patches on lake bottoms, or shoals. A number of aquatic plants have *weed* as a part of their common names, such as the "pond weeds" *(Potamogeton Spp.),* but others not ordinarily called weeds may be grouped as such when they occur in dense patches in lakes. "Weed beds" are regarded as useful, or valuable, components of lakes in that they provide food and shelter for fish, waterfowl, and other aquatic animals. However, where the growth be-

Dense growth of *Myriophyllum* chokes outboard motors. Photo by Bevin, Chesapeake Biological Laboratory, courtesy *Virginia Wildlife*, March, 1964.

comes excessively prolific the beds can be a cause of fish mortality, interfere with boating, swimming, and otherwise become a nuisance.

weed cutter, underwater

A motor operated underwater cutting bar used to remove aquatic plants. Some small models are designed for private owners to use in a row boat and other large heavy models have to be mounted on a barge. Aquatic vegetation can be cut off at the desired water depth or along the bottom in shallow water.

weeds (lake)

According to prevailing usage, weeds applied to some aquatic species growing in lakes, implies that the plants are obnoxious or a nuisance. However, usage in a derogatory sense is not uniform and quite as often the popular name weed may be retained for a plant that serves a useful purpose.

well

Where a large excavation has been made into the zone of saturation and is consequently filled with water to the level of the ground water table, such an artificial feature may be regarded with equal validity as either a small *pond* or simply as a great open well.

wet beach

See: *beach profile* for illustration

The area of a beach below the waterline covered by ordinary wave water.

Dry beach ⟶ | ⟵ Wet beach
Storm beach

wet prairies

The word "prairie" has been applied to various kinds of wetland in the eastern part of the United States. Marshes of various kinds including some permanently covered by water and supporting aquatic vegetation, and floating marshes or *flotant* have been called prairie, wet prairie and water prairie. Also, the hydronym water prairie has been applied to open watery expanses in forested swamps; and the beds of intermittent lakes and those of extinct lakes have been called prairies under certain circumstances.

wetlands

The term *wetlands,* for a broad group of wet habitats, is in common use by specialists in the field of wild life, especially water fowl management. It includes features that are permanently wet, or intermittently water covered, such as swamps, marshes, bogs, muskegs, potholes, swales, glades, slashes, and overflow land of river valleys. Large open lakes are commonly excluded, but many kinds of ponds, pools, sloughs, holes and bayous may be included.

wharfage right

The inherent right of a riparian to construct a wharf or boat dock from the shore out to deep water as a convenience for the use of boats.

This also includes the right of a riparian to launch, anchor, tie up or beach a boat from his land.

wide water

A localism in the northern part of Michigan for a widening in the course of a river, or for a wide shallow expanse of water backed up by some kind of natural dam. However, *wide water* (or *Wide Waters,* or *The Wide Water*) appears in only a few instances on maps as a place name.

widespread

See: *spread*

width (of a lake)

The *maximum width* of a lake is the measure of a line connecting the most remote extremities of the water surface and crossing the maximum length axis at approximately right angles. The *mean width* is the area of the lake divided by its maximum length.

See: *breadth*

wilderness lakes

The name "wilderness" may be used for those lakes whose shores and waters remain unmodified by man, or

Photo – Michigan Department of Conservation

A wilderness lake. Porcupine Mountains, Michigan.

essentially in a virgin condition. The name may be applied regardless of geographic location, that is such lakes do not necessarily have to be located in a wilderness region.

Because of improved accessibility some lakes in so-called wilderness or primitive regions have not escaped modification or even pollution.

wildfowl sanctuary

It is possible to dedicate certain lands, waters, and lakes as wildfowl sanctuaries; the taking of wildfowl is forbidden.

wild rice

Zizania aquatica — An aquatic grass, fairly common in northern lakes, both as a native and a planted species. Its grain was an important source of food for American In-

Wild rice in a Michigan lake.

dians and is highly prized at present by gourmets. It is also a source of food for wild fowl. On the other hand its growth in some lakes may become so prolific that it impedes boating and thereby becomes a nuisance. A brief statement about its original distribution in Michigan can be found in the publication: *The Aboriginal Population of Michigan*, W. B. Hinsdale, page 21, published by University of Michigan Press, 1932.

wind streaks

Linear accumulations of foam and floating debris; sometimes observed on the surfaces of large lakes. A phenomenon of wind drift.

Wind streaks on a lake.

wind seiche

See: *seiche*

windward shore
The shore which faces the prevailing wind. It is thus often exposed to strong wave action with resulting shore erosion and beach formation.

winged headland
A headland, or promontory, with spits projecting from its sides.

winter kill
Partial or complete loss of the fish population of a lake in winter due to the formation of a complete ice cover.

See: *fish kill*
freeze-out lake

yield (of a lake)
(1) The quantity of water which can be taken, continuously, for any particular economic use. (2) The measure of the crops, plant and animal, which a lake produces naturally or under management.

young lakes
Lakes in a youthful stage of physiographic development. In these lakes, the shore erosion, filling by aquatic vegetation and shoreline recession characteristic of *mature* and *old* lakes is not in evidence.

zooplankton
Animal microorganisms living unattached in the water.

See: *plankton*

zonation

Ecologists and limnologists recognize "zones" of life in lakes and on the bordering lake bottom backland (representing former stages or levels in the lake). The "zones", rarely sharply delineated or rarely forming a continuous belt around the whole lake basin, bear a relation to: depths of light penetration and oxygen content of water; gradients of bottom and increase in the depth from the shoreline lakeward; composition of bottom deposits; and the time lapsed since recession and the exposure of the lake bottom as land surface.

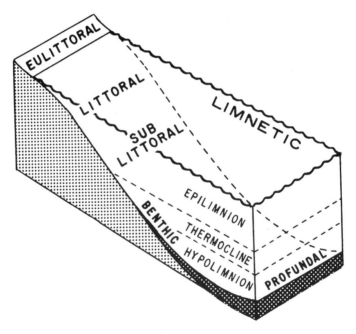

Zonation

zoning (lakeland)

The application to water frontage and shore land, of legal restrictions pertaining to the use of land in such matters as size of building lots, cost of cottages, nature and location of business establishments, roadways and to other things affecting property values.

Zoning as such, is not applied to the water area of lakes, but zoning which affects the use of the shoreland may indirectly affect the use of the water. In some states, governmental agencies have been given authority to stipulate the kind of use that can be made of the lake surface at designated times.

USE AREAS OF A LAKELAND

1. Backland use zone
2. Littoral use zone
3. Open water use zone

Appendix

SHORE CLASSIFICATION

(Special reference to Michigan lakes and to shore as a natural resource)

A. HIGH SHORE (Cliff rising from shoreline)
  1. Rock cliff
     a. Storm beach and littoral shelf absent
     b. Storm beach and littoral shelf present
     c. Beach present, littoral shelf absent
  2. Glacial drift cliff
     a. Storm beach and littoral shelf absent
     b. Storm beach and littoral shelf present
     c. Beach present, littoral shelf absent
  3. Dunes
     a. Beach present
     b. Beach absent

B. LOW SHORE (Cliff not present at shoreline)
  1. Hard shore (beach, beach ridge, berm, shore bench)
     a. Sand beach
        (1) Wide littoral shelf, sand bottom
        (2) Narrow shelf; bottom steep gradient
     b. Pebble, cobble, shingle and rubble beach
        (1) Wide littoral shelf
        (2) Narrow shelf, or bottom steep gradient
     c. Boulder shore
        (1) Wide littoral shelf bouldery
        (2) Narrow littoral shelf
     d. Bed rock, boulder shore
        (1) Wide shoal bottom, stony
        (2) Narrow shelf

   2. Soft shore
     a. Peat - muck
      (1) Shallow mud bottom
      (2) Narrow shelf or drop off at shore
     b. Marl
      (1) Wide soft bottom
      (2) Narrow shelf or drop off
     c. Clay
      (1) Wide shelf soft bottom bouldery
      (2) Wide shelf, not bouldery
      (3) Narrow shelf and drop off

C. RECESSION SHORE. Wide zone of recently exposed lake bottom between the water margin and the former shoreline.

D. ARTIFICIAL. Fills of all kinds; mine tailings, lumber mill refuse, dredging spoils, sea walls, etc.

E. SHORE VEGETATION
   1. Marsh shore
   2. Quaking bog, false shore
   3. Shrub shore
   4. Swamp forest shore
   5. Wooded shore (upland trees)
   6. Marginal water (weed shore)
     a. Shallow water border
     b. Shelf with drop off and deep open water border.
   7. Artificial: grassed, planted trees and shrubs.

ILLUSTRATIONS FOR SHORELINE CLASSIFICATION

Photo — Michigan Tourist Council

Rock Cliff

A. HIGH SHORE
    1. Rock cliff rising from waterline
        b. Storm beach present

A. HIGH SHORE (Cliff rising from shoreline)
    2. Glacial drift cliff
        a. Storm beach and littoral shelf absent

A. HIGH SHORE (Cliff rising from shoreline)
2. Glacial drift cliff
b. Sand storm beach and littoral shelf present

A. HIGH SHORE (Cliff rising from shoreline)
2. Glacial drift cliff
b. Shingle storm beach

A. HIGH SHORE (Cliff rising from shoreline)
   3. Dunes
      a. Beach present

B. LOW SHORE (Cliff not present at shoreline)
   1. Hard shore
      a. Sand beach

B. LOW SHORE
   1. Hard shore
      b. Pebble beach

B. LOW SHORE
   1. Hard shore
      b. Cobble beach

B. LOW SHORE
  1. Hard shore
    d. Boulder shore

B. LOW SHORE
  2. Soft shore
    a. Muck

B.   LOW SHORE
    2. Soft shore
       b. Marl

B.   LOW SHORE
    2. Soft shore
       c. Clay

C. RECESSION SHORE. Wide zone of recently exposed lake bottom between the water margin and the former shoreline.

D. ARTIFICIAL. Fills of all kinds; mine tailings, lumber mill refuse, dredging spoils, sea walls, etc.

Land fill for cottages.

Shoreland used for a dump.

Beach fill.

E. SHORE VEGETATION
   1. Marsh shore

Photo — Michigan Department of Conservation

E. SHORE VEGETATION
    2. Quaking bog, false shore

Photo — Davis, C. A. *Peat*, Michigan Geological Survey, Lansing, Michigan, 1906.

E. SHORE VEGETATION
    3. Shrub shore

374

E. SHORE VEGETATION
    4. Swamp forest shore

E. SHORE VEGETATION
    6. Marginal water (weed shore)
        a. shallow water border

E.   SHORE VEGETATION
    6. Marginal water (weed shore)
       b. Shelf with drop off and deep open water border.

References

The student who desires full information on limnological matters is referred to the following books:

1. *Treatise on Limnology*, Volume I, by G. E. Hutchinson, published by John Wiley, New York, 1957.
2. *Limnology*, by P. S. Welch, second edition, published by Mc Graw-Hill, New York, 1952.
3. *Ecology of Inland Waters and Estuaries*, by George K. Reid, published by Reinhold Publishing Corporation, New York, 1961.
4. *Fundamentals of Limnology*, by Franz Ruttner, translated by D. G. Frey and F. E. J. Frey, published by University of Toronto Press, Toronto, Canada, 1953.

The following publications are valuable sources of information, especially for the Northern Lake State region.

1. Inland Lakes of Michigan, by I. D. Scott, 1920, Michigan Geological Survey, Pub. 30, Series 25.
2. Inland Lakes of Wisconsin, by C. Juday, 1914, Bulletin Wisconsin Geological Survey 27, Series No. 9.
3. The Lakes of Minnesota, by J. H. Zumberge, University of Minnesota Press, Minneapolis, 1952.

An extensive list of publications pertaining to Michigan waters is available in Water Bulletin No. 13, Michigan Inland Lake Reference List, published by the Department of Resource Development and the Agricultural Experiment Station, Michigan State University, 1963.

ACKNOWLEDGEMENTS

The authors extend thanks to Keith V. Slack, Limnologist, U. S. Geological Survey, Washington, D. C. and to C. W. Threinen, Administrative Assistant, Wisconsin Conservation Department, who reviewed the original manuscript and made helpful criticisms; and wish to acknowledge helpful suggestions from colleagues at Michigan State University.

We are grateful, too, to Mr. J. Paul Schneider for the line drawings.

JETHRO OTTO VEATCH

His students affectionately, with respect and esteem refer to J. O. as the "grand old man" of conservation. As a soil scientist, after his graduation from the University of Missouri in 1909, he was assigned as a special investigator in the Bureau of Soils, by Dr. C. F. Marbut to study soil classification and genesis. His publications resulting from this effort are found in 88 bulletins and technical articles dealing with the soils of Texas, Alabama, Georgia, South Carolina, Florida, Pennsylvania, Iowa, Nebraska, Wyoming and Michigan.

In 1953, three years after his academic retirement, *Soils and Land of Michigan,* was published. It is widely used in the Lake states as a reference but it is also found on the bookshelves of many small private libraries of the more worldly natural scientists.

Conservation administrators and students alike have frequently felt the sharp and penetrating impact of his critical, technical and philosophical analysis. His written contributions are recorded in published works but his contributions to students and colleagues are alive and working today to improve an understanding of natural resources. Few of J. O.'s students are likely to ever forget him or his lectures which reflected his keen insight as a careful scientist — geologist, geographer, soil scientist, ecologist, economist, social philosopher, scholar and teacher. His statements and random thoughts suddenly become relevant to new situations and problems in distant parts of the world.

Over a period of 44 years of field observations, J. O. has carefully collected and recorded pragmatic information concerning water resources. Many of these notes were recorded upon odd slips and pieces of paper which would defy interpretation except by all but his closest associates. After his retirement these old notes and new field observations were expanded, polished and illustrated as entries for this book. Many of the entries are more truly essays of outstanding clarity and depth of understanding. His work in the field of water resources is relevant and pertinent to the vast challenge we face today with the development, use and management of water, and will in all probability be more remembered than his efforts in soil science.

CLIFFORD ROBERTSON HUMPHRYS

His career commenced with a Forestry Degree at Michigan State University. The depression of 1929 left upon him a lasting impression of the importance of resource management and a need for the intangible aesthetic values in the lives of men. Advanced work in soil genesis and classification permitted an exploration of geology, game management and engineering. While a graduate student, he was employed by the United States Department of Agriculture, Bureau of Plant Industry, Soils and Agricultural Engineering, as a Soil Surveyor and Soil Scientist for seven years. During World War II he served as a Photographic Interpretation Officer with the United States Navy for four and one-half years with duty in those theaters where amphibious warfare was prevalent; South Pacific, European and Far East.

Employment with the Michigan Department of Conservation started as a land appraiser in the acquisition section of the Lands Division and terminated later as mineral leasing executive. This experience focused upon the varying needs and philosophies of conservation practices. It was during this period, that he became deeply impressed with the function of politics and law as applied to management policy for natural resources.

By 1953, when he joined the staff of the Department of Land and Water Conservation at Michigan State University, his goals were crystalized as a water resource specialist. Courses now taught by him are limited to Water Resource Development for undergraduates and Watershed Management for graduate students.

PUBLICATIONS —

Books

Lake Terminology, J. O. Veatch and C. R. Humphrys
Michigan Lakes and Ponds, C. R. Humphrys, et al.
Analysis of the Red Cedar River, C. R. Humphrys, et al.

Bulletins

Coauthor for four Michigan County Soil Survey Reports
Lakeshore Classification Bulletins for 30 Michigan Counties
Lake Inventory Bulletins for 83 Michigan Counties
Series of 18 Water Bulletins

Articles

Numerous articles for journals, magazines and newspapers.

Professor Humphrys frequently serves as a consultant for the United States Navy, insurance companies, lawyers, lake developers, artificial lake companies and County Drain Commissions. His work on the Boundary Waters Canoe Area, for the United States Forest Service in 1964 was culminated by the private publication of *The Lost Lakes of Minnesota*, dealing with the problems of the most magnificent lake region in this country. Consultant work frequently exposes a specialist to controversial issues on the firing line of conservation practice.

Students frequently grumble about the length of his reading assignments and his insistence upon the exploration of all facets of water resources and their related problems. All agree, however, that no effort is spared to challenge their pre-conceived ideals and to introduce other views concerning water resource management. Tests usually involve a soul searching personal evaluation of isolated water topics that demand organized reflection and thought. By the time of the scheduled final examination, both student and instructor have been exposed to the fires of new doctrine, theory and philosophy.

Critics are apt to rebel against his frontal attack upon pertinent water problems. On occasion he is subtly aggressive or idealistic in his approach to the expedient solution of water problems. His effort would appear to be focused upon the exploration of new approaches for new problems.

The introduction of a man with his great variety of physical and moral needs into the field of water resources imposes a challenge to the technical water resource manager of the future. He argues that the intangible and aesthetic qualities of water must also be considered if this challenge is met successfully. Man's need is not limited to H_2O, the mineral, but involves the total water environment, including all the fragile, intangible and intrinsic values of a lake or stream environment.

As a "loner" without professional affiliation or loyalty to any particular art, science or group, he exerts new and refreshing pressures upon the examination of water resources, dealing not only with the physical qualities of water but also with man as a vital part of the complex issue of water management. In class or after a speech he frequently closes with the remark — "There would be no water problems if there were no people."